THE TIBETAN ART

THE TIBETAN ART OF LIVING

Wise body

Wise mind

Wise life

CHRISTOPHER HANSARD

HODDER
MOBIUS

Hodder & Stoughton

This book is intended as a guide to people who want to improve and maintain their health. If you are concerned in any way about your health, you should seek medical advice.

Copyright © 2001 by Christopher Hansard

First published in Great Britain in 2001 by Hodder and Stoughton
Paperback edition first published in 2002 by Hodder & Stoughton
A division of Hodder Headline

The right of Christopher Hansard to be identified as the Author of the Work has been
asserted by him in accordance with the Copyright, Designs and Patents Act 1988.

8   10   9   7

A CIP catalogue record for this title is available from the British Library

ISBN 0 340 77124 0

Typeset in Poliphilus and Blado Italic by
Palimpsest Book Production Limited, Polmont, Stirlingshire
Printed and bound in Great Britain by
Mackays of Chatham plc, Chatham, Kent

Hodder and Stoughton
A division of Hodder Headline
338 Euston Road
London NW1 3BH

Dedication

The knowledge in this book is dedicated to the Masters of the Twelve Lores Of Bön and the lineages of dMu and Dur. To the Ngagpa of the Nam or 'Sky' clan and its lineage a thousand blessings are offered up. I dedicate this book to those that read it, may they find lasting happiness.

On a personal note, I dedicate this book to my beautiful wife Silvia and my exquisite daughter, Flavia, who supported me with encouragement and love through the process of writing.

Contents

Acknowledgements

I would like to acknowledge the valuable support of the following people who made it possible for me to have time to write this book. They are Christopher Walls, Sharon Seager and Dr Stephanie Wright.

I would like to thank Fiona Harrold for making introductions and a most wonderful, enthusiastic and genuine publisher, Rowena Webb. I would like to thank Rosemary Trapnell, Briar Silich and the Art Director at Hodder, Ian Hughes, for all his care and attention to detail. Also my thanks to Samantha Evans, Katy Follain and Jamie Hodder-Williams. Also to everyone else at Hodder whom I have depended upon; thank you. No book is a solo effort.

My agent, Kay McCauley, I give deep thanks to for helping me on the way to becoming a writer, for her friendship and mentorship.

Also a deeply important acknowledgement must go to Sarah Stacey, both a brilliant writer in her own regard and an amazing editor who went beyond the call of duty to reveal all the essences of this profound subject while still keeping much of my original text in place. This book could not have been done without her. To Sarah goes my deep-felt thanks and respect for her guidance in helping me to learn about writing.

PREFACE

The Song of Wisdom

The fire burnt slowly, throwing sparks up into the sunset. The aroma of juniper filled the air, a sacred offering to the god-energies of ancient Tibet. The vibrations from the low chanting of my teacher spread out from the hilltop on top of Mount Pihanga, where I sat with him. They drifted down into the valley below, blending with the mist.

We were in an area of mountains and lakes in the Taupo region of New Zealand's North Island. It had been sacred to the local Maori people for over a thousand years. In the last light, a river snaking out of a lake glistened palely in the dark surrounding forest. Then night came. Stars leapt out of the void, each one fire bright, each one singing in response to the chant.

My teacher was deep in the flow, his face a study of concentration and stillness. I added more juniper berries and branches to the fire. The flames leapt up as if they were jumping into space. The fire seemed to act as a conduit between heaven and earth, purified by juniper, empowered by chanting.

Picking up a small flat drum, Ürgyen, my teacher, slowly began to move his fingers in long, drawn-out circles over the worn skin. The sound of his fingertips whispered, sussurated. Suddenly a roar burst from the drum, hung in the air, then fell back again, becoming a drone under the words of the chant. A sudden wind blew around us, a continuous stream of magically invoked air. The drum and the wind sounded as one, flowing from the hill out into the wider world.

<~>

The hilltop became the only hilltop in the world.
The darkness below was a deep sea of energy.
The energy common to everything that lives and
*   feels.*

My mind journeyed into that dark sea, borne by the
    words of the chant.
Words from the ancient times of Tibet — of power
    and blessing, of rebirth and creation.
Words that free the mind.
Words that destroy ignorance and cast out fear.
Words of healing for every living thing that hears
    them.

<~>

That night I heard the songs of the earth and the elements. The words talked of what we are made of, where we came from and where we are going to. Of how things are. They were songs of wisdom, a wisdom that lies at the foundation of all humanity.

All living things can hear that wisdom. They knew the song my teacher was singing that night. They knew it because they were the words and the wisdom. We know the song, too. Because we are the words. We are the wisdom.

<~>

In that night, I began to understand and experience the wisdom, healing and power of this chant, dedicated to endless compassion and wisdom. According to ancient Tibetan belief, it was first sung by the earliest non-human inhabitants of Tibet, known as the Masang, who existed well before the dawn of human beings.

The chant was a profound step in my training as a physician of Tibetan Dür Bön Medicine. After 23 years, spiritual and medical teachings were finally merging as one. As he chanted, my teacher was passing on a spiritual empowerment. The energy released in the process transformed and expanded my psyche, mind and body. My attachments to my imperfections, prejudices and obstructions began to dissipate.

<~>

The slow droning of the drum reached into every part of me, re-organising the way I was made, making inner space for consciousness, making room for my humanity to grow, creating spiritual bonds with everything that I had learnt from my teacher since childhood.

This would be the last year of my teacher's life. He brought many important lessons for me, and I remembered when we first met in New Zealand in 1961. I was on a beach at Rona Bay, Wellington. I was four years old, out for a day by the sea with my parents.

The tide was slowly receding and the sea fell in long gentle waves along the grey-brown sand. Already there were people in the shallow water gathering small shellfish to cook for their evening meal. Seagulls wheeled and hung expectantly in the wind as I walked along the beach towards the faded weather-beaten pier.

All that day I felt something important was going to happen, something I felt I already knew but did not have the language to express. My parents called me to leave, to go home. But inside me, I knew I could not go yet.

'I have to stay here.'

'Come on, its time to go.'

'No, I have to stay.'

'Why?'

I didn't know what to say. All my words and thoughts were a jumble. I trudged towards my parents. Then, as we mounted the edge of the beach onto the gravel road, I saw my teacher standing there, waiting. A rainbow appeared and he laughed.

Ürgyen Nam Chuk introduced himself to my parents. He explained that he represented a Tibetan spiritual and medical tradition which, among other tools, used a profound system of astrology. This had suggested that I might be a possible candidate to receive education from the Tibetan Bön spiritual and medical tradition.

My parents weren't impressed at first. But as they got to know Ürgyen and understood that he was not looking for handouts of any kind they felt more at ease. They began to understand how important it was for me, and allowed me to go through the next stage, which was a number of tests and spiritual questions to determine whether the astrological process was correct.

My parents were aware of the Tibetan tradition of incarnating spiritual teachers but Ürgyen explained that he did not regard me as one of these, but someone who, with training, had the potential to develop rare and special abilities related to medicine, healing and spirituality in the Bön tradition. I was not regarded as perfect or special, and would not be encouraged to think like this.

My teacher

Ürgyen Nam Chuk was well known as a Bön Ngagpa, a married man of high spiritual calibre. The Ngagpa tradition is found in most of the various Tibetan spiritual legacies from the four Buddhist schools of thought and all the Bön traditions. They are instantly identifiable by their hair, which is worn long and uncut, either in a topknot or in dreadlocks.

Ngagpas have always been regarded as the spiritual geniuses of Tibet, wild, unpredictable and incredible. My teacher was like this. This meant that as I grew older I had to be observant and aware in order to avoid practical jokes, booby traps and the general mayhem that was subtly intertwined with the long hours of discipline, study and hard work.

Traditionally, Ngagpas look after their communities by performing birth rituals, weddings, funerals and divinations. They also perform a wide range of other rituals, simple and complicated, for the protection and benefit of the community. All Ngagpas are credited with having power over and with the forces of nature. The weather and the harvest come under their aegis, for example, as do the dispensation of justice and sometimes warfare. Some are also experts in martial arts, some master physicians and others great spiritual masters. Ürgyen was one of the few who had developed all of these qualities.

He came from the partly nomadic Nam clan, which had originally entered Tibet from Lake Baikal in Siberia well over 800 years ago. They were famous for their medical skills, spiritual teaching and psychic powers. Although they were partly nomadic, they intermarried with local people and finally settled permanently in a province of Tibet named Amdo. Another group based themselves in Nangchen Gar, a small self-ruling kingdom within Tibet, which became an important spiritual centre for the Ngagpa tradition.

The entire clan left Tibet in 1916, almost 40 years before China invaded Tibet. An important master within the Nam lineage had prophesied the invasion and – with others – tried in vain to warn the Tibetan authorities. The complete Nam clan moved from Tibet and, under instruction from the head of the clan, split into various units so that each could look after a special part of their culture and set up a trade network.

Some went to Nepal, a few to Leh and the little kingdom of Lo, while others went to Himachal Pradesh, a state in India. Others journeyed to Sikkim, and to another state of India called Arunachal Pradesh, or to Calcutta, Bombay, Varanasi and Madras. The people who represented the spiritual core of the Nam clan kept themselves secure in remote parts of Sikkim, and the Kingdom of Lo. As my teacher grew up, he travelled between all of these places to gain inner knowledge, and he was also involved in managing the wealth of the clan.

Every year, astrological divinations were carried out concerning the spiritual teachings of Bön. Eventually it was decided that for the teachings to continue suitable people must be found outside the clan, perhaps even outside the Tibetan community. The divinatory masters built a structure on the ground representing the earth and the astrological influences and, after much study, directed my teacher, then in his late thirties, to search in the Southern hemisphere for a suitable person. He arrived in New Zealand four years before I was born.

Early days

From the age of four, I spent the next 23 years of my life learning the spiritual and medical knowledge of ancient Tibet. My family had moved from Wellington to Auckland by then, and I went to a normal Western school and was a typical naughty boy. My teacher followed and I saw him at the beginning and end of week days, and on the weekends.

At eight my formal Tibetan medical education began, alongside the spiritual disciplines I had been learning since I was four. I also learned the Bön version of the exercise system called Kum Nye, which consists of eight exercises designed to transform the mind and body, clearing obstructions, improving physical strength and health, and preparing the student for the higher stages of learning.

We are our own healers

'To heal someone, you must first know why people suffer,' my teacher said. 'If, through healing them, you can show them how to stop suffering, you have fulfilled your role as a physician.'

I learned that at the heart of all suffering there is a spiritual remedy that comes about from knowing the relationships between karma and suffering. Karma comes from the chaos that exists within all living creatures, all aspects of this world and the universe at large. Some chaos is good, some indifferent, some bad, but it is the stuff from which happiness and then enlightenment can be made.

By transforming chaos within the mind and body, the physician of Tibetan Medicine gives the patient opportunities for healing, happiness and wisdom. Meditation and the generation of compassion are at the heart of this body of knowledge because, without these resources, knowledge could easily be used in unskilful ways.

Healing is not taught. It is a continual stream of energy that flows from human consciousness into the natural and man-made world. Through the techniques, observations and theories of Tibetan medicine, you can learn to connect with this continual stream of healing.

Healing is another aspect of love, of an expanding compassion that comes from a drive for consciousness to seek itself. In the world, the universe, and within ourselves, consciousness seeks to bring all chaos into balance, so that matter, time and space will disappear into a continual flow of harmony. Healing is not just making a sick person better; it is about making that person more conscious.

Healing is also an act of self-knowledge. We are our own healers. When we know that we need healing, we activate the healing within us: this awakens knowledge about who we are. This can also be stimulated by the physician responding to a patient's request for help.

As I studied, my self-knowledge matured (at least in my own mind) and my awareness of the immensity of Tibetan medicine increased, year by year. At fourteen, I took the vow that all Tibetan physicians take in my tradition: 'I vow to work until I am no longer needed, when illness in all its forms and guises has gone, and all living beings have achieved lasting happiness.'

<~>

The moon rose high upon a garland of stars, its light spreading faintly across the sky. I could see the river and lake below me. The firelight splashed across my teacher's face showed his deep state of meditation. Occasionally, shooting stars rushed past.

'Each one is a soul coming back to birth again,' he said softly.

I found myself reflecting silently on the strangeness of this experience. Sitting on a sacred mountain in the sacred land of the Maori people, learning Tibetan sacred teachings with the blessings of Maori elders on my teacher. Making sense of it all seemed a challenge.

My teacher knew my mind. 'Don't deny your own culture, learn from it as much as you can,' he said. 'Try to bring a unity between what I have tried to teach you and what is in the West.'

His words activated a growing and changing consciousness within me. I felt a blending of energies within me of West and East: Tibet and the Antipodes, Bön and New Zealander — ancient knowledge from the top of the world delivered to a young man in a young country perched at its end.

CHRISTOPHER HANSARD
LONDON, 2001

CHAPTER ONE

How Tibetan Wisdom Sees the World

This book is about how Tibetan medicine can help you to create wisdom, health and well-being. It is not for scholars: there are already books of that kind by people well versed in the subject. This is primarily a book of self-exploration; which uses Tibetan medicine as a guide on the path to knowledge of your self.

We should regard ourselves as pilgrims following an inner journey that is beautiful, scary and sometimes difficult. In these pages, you will learn about the art of living. You will discover many safe, traditional self-healing techniques that will empower you to become healthy and happy. Above all, you will experience the profound healing system within your being. So that you can become your own best healer.

Understanding any culture can be difficult if you have not learned the thinking process behind it. It is the same with Tibetan medicine, which has its own special thinking process and language. In order for this book to be useful to you, it is important to know and experience the underlying world view that is at the heart of one of the world's most sophisticated systems of healing.

Tibetan medicine is an ancient and detailed system that aims to unite the mind, body and inner spirit of an ill person and so restore a dynamic balance. It works to create patterns of health by helping people change their mental and behavioural attitudes, even if the problem is a physical injury such as a broken leg. This does not mean that everything is in the mind. What Tibetan medicine does is to help people to understand the origins and cause of an illness, and how we hold illness in both our bodies and in our minds.

By understanding why you are ill, why you have pain, why you suffer, you become stronger and wiser. You start to understand how and why any overwhelming or obstructive experience expresses itself as mental or physical illness. You then know how to stop suffering and heal both your illness and the way you live.

THE ORIGINS OF TIBETAN DUR BÖN MEDICINE

Tibetan spirituality in all its forms goes back to a simple and basic belief that has existed in the peoples of Tibet since the most ancient times. In order to gain spiritual growth you must first gain personal vitality and energy. This will make you strong and free from obstructions so that you attract only good things toward you. This concept lies at the heart of all religious and spiritual thought of the Tibetan religious experience.

There are two structured religious teachings in Tibetan culture today. One is Buddhism and the other Bön, a Tibetan term that basically means 'to invoke a deity'. According to the Bön tradition, the great spiritual genius Tonpa Shenrab Miwo, who was born 17,000 years before the historical Buddha, founded the Bön teaching. As a fully enlightened person from birth, he was able to give teachings that helped people to cure their suffering.

Both Tonpa Shenrab Miwo and Buddha were regarded as master physicians because they diagnosed the root causes of suffering. They developed similar ideas about how to transform suffering, encourage happiness and create inner balance. They understood the human condition.

The original practitioners of Dur Bön, from which my tradition developed, were married priests in pre-Buddhist times; their job was to prepare the bodies of dead kings and escort their souls to higher states of consciousness. They were advisors to royal families and important community leaders, and also held complex medical knowledge about how the body and mind worked and how it died and reformed. This medical knowledge came from an older culture known as Zhang Zhung.

The Dur Bön school merged with a spiritual tradition known as dMu T'ang, which is also part of the Bön culture. In its earliest times dMu T'ang trained its exponents to send their minds out into other realms of consciousness. This skill was used to heal, guide and protect the community. The dMu T'ang tradition also held important spiritual and medical teachings in the forms of physical and mental exercises.

The practitioners of Dur Bön and dMu T'ang were known as mystics, philosophers, physicians and scientists. Their legacy extended to all schools of Bön and has influenced Tibetan Buddhism as well. Rningmapa, the oldest school of Tibetan Buddhism, is similar to some aspects of Bön culture. Modern research suggests that many aspects of Indian and Chinese culture have borrowed much from Bön. The origins of Hinduism and the Taoist and Feng Shui philosophies of China all emanate from Bön culture and spirituality.

When Buddhism first came to Tibet in the seventh century, it made little impact. In the eighth century AD, however, the government was in crisis and there was unrest among the Bön nobility. The Buddhists launched a well-planned military invasion and succeeded in becoming the dominant religion in Tibet until the Chinese invasion of 1959.

At first, the two systems of thinking – Buddhist and Bön – got on well together. Then, however, certain Buddhist factions started to persecute Bön communities. To stop the persecution, some Bön communities took on the trappings of the Buddhist teaching and developed into what became known as 'Reformed Bön'. These people are called Bön-pos. In reality, however, their teachings are much the same and there is little controversy between the two approaches. The search for virtue, compassion and wisdom is the same for Buddhists and all forms of Bön communities. My teacher, who was a Bön master and taught me the old Bön (the Bön of the Ngagpas), married a woman from a famous family of Buddhist teachers. He and his wife suffered no division in their spiritual practices or religious views.

His Holiness the Dalai Lama has recently taken a significant step in uniting the fabric of Tibet by acknowledging the crucial role of Bön in defining Tibetan culture. Those in the West who know anything about Bön tend to get it mixed up with indigenous Tibetan shamanism and animistic beliefs. This is inaccurate but, confusingly, both Buddhism and Bön endorse some, if not all, of those beliefs and have incorporated them into their way of thinking.

Indeed, all Tibetan teachings have succeeded in keeping their vitality and universal truths. Although Tibetan Buddhism is far better known today than Bön, there are still thousands of practitioners in Tibet and throughout the Himalayan region, and there are Bön religious communities in India, Eastern Tibet, North America and some parts of Central Asia.

Currently, all religious activity in Tibet is outlawed. The official religion today is the mindless adherence to Chinese Communism. But Buddhist and Bön communities are not the only ones to suffer from Communist persecution. The Tibetan Muslims, Jews and Christians have all suffered terribly.

 How WE SEE THE WORLD

According to Tibetan medicine, the body is a physical expression of mental energies generated by the brain. The nature of these energies is created by the way each person interprets the world around them.

Although we think that we are reacting instantaneously to everything that happens to us, we are, in fact, always living in the past because our brains can only react through our senses. Consider this, and you'll see that your reaction is always a few seconds behind the event because of the time it takes to process via your senses and brain. Our sense of immediacy is an illusion. What we think is happening right now has already passed.

In the same way, illness creates an illusion about its nature, and it is this illusion that we need to see through. We are conditioned psycho-logically to expect to be ill. Because we live in this potent expectation, illness follows us like a stubborn dog that refuses to be sent home. Illness is a self-fulfilling prophecy.

How illness builds up in our bodies

Over time, negative or extremely intense experiences, good or bad times, slowly stun the body and mind. They infiltrate the central nervous system of our bodies and leave their influence behind in the form of deeply rooted energies that abide in the deepest parts of our person-ality. Here, according to Tibetan medicine, these old influences build and create emotional and spiritual garbage that, in time, become physical and emotional illness or negative life circumstances.

These subtle underlying forces of ill-health relate to something called 'karma'. The way we react to the stimuli around us, and the illusion we have of living in the present, create the causes and condi-tions of our lives. This is karma.

Karma can be defined as a conscious mental decision and action carried out for a particular end result. Everyday we create karma by experiencing problems, coping with stress, eating or drinking too much, and even having too much of a good or bad time – when we are angry, lie, cause trouble for other people, or cause ourselves harm by acting before thinking things through. All of these daily experiences that we go through leave their imprints in our minds and bodies, on our lives and on those of other people. You will find a fuller explanation of karma in Chapter 3.

So how can we try to overcome this dilemma?

Health is a process

According to the Tibetans, health is like a tide. It is a process, not a static or constant experience. Each person's state of energy is continuously changing from one moment to the next, rising and falling, increasing and decreasing. When energy falls below a certain level, which differs from person to person, the first signs of illness are experienced.

Illness can take a long time to find its way into material form and may not be obvious. Many people go about their daily lives looking perfectly healthy on the outside, yet within they may have a deep-seated emotional problem or an unseen cancer carrying them closer to death. Some people allow stress, one of the most damaging influences on our health in modern times, to fester and build up inside so that years, even decades later, they find themselves burnt out and ill.

Preventing the causes of illness means knowing how to prevent unskilful patterns of emotions and behaviour so that our lives become more harmonious and balanced. You will meet the concept of skilful and unskilful behaviour frequently in this book. In a nutshell, skilful behaviour leads to positive outcomes, unskilful to negativity.

Negativity and prejudice are closely related. People are united more by their prejudices – of every kind – than by any other common factor. Prejudice represses anyone who experiences it into a state of worth-lessness and triviality. Illness can be seen as a prejudice that you have created towards yourself. By understanding how we think about ourselves, we learn how we create the foundations of health and illness and this in turn will show us how we create our own subconscious patterns of karma.

 ## YOUR LIFE IS A SPIRITUAL EXPERIENCE

We see ourselves as flesh and blood but, in fact, human beings are consciousness that has sought a way to express itself in this material world by taking on a physical form. Underneath all the physical and mental construction of daily life on this planet lies a pure and open spiritual consciousness. This is a natural state of mind that is always there within every person, entwined in the fabric of our lives.

This duality can create chaos and suffering. Illness is often brought about by our minds, emotions and habits getting in the way of the pure consciousness at our core. But our innate spirituality can also create order and beauty.

Realising that each of us has this infinite potential is at the heart of Tibetan spiritual teaching. It exists in everyone and everything. At this very moment, you are the great symbol of your own potential enlightenment.

The purpose of any spiritual practice, ethical framework or religious belief should be to help us enjoy the life that we have. What's important is to avoid getting caught up with the future, because the future – and the past – are only creations of our imagination. To be happy we need first to allow ourselves to be so – now. So forget thoughts like 'I will be so happy *if only* that would happen . . .' and, 'I was so happy *when* things were different . . .'. All you have is now. So accept yourself as you are without embellishment or regret.

Start by aiming to experience everyday life in as open and direct a manner as possible. From the moment you wake to the moment you sleep, allow every experience to come to you without judgement. The key is acceptance.

Accepting whatever happens is a hard place to be at first. Like everyone, you will feel fear at the very idea, but gradually, as you cut through the barriers developed by years of habit, you will start to become less reactive to the world around you. We often live our whole lives in a state of reaction to experiences. If we are caused pain, we become angry, we hurt, we cry, we fear for our existence. These reactive responses continue the subtle links of our own suffering. Whether they are big events in our lives or small ones, the end result is the same.

Acceptance takes the sting out of reactivity and creates for us insight into the way we make our lives happen. An experience of great simplicity will emerge from your consciousness as you allow accept-ance to filter into all your mental and physical actions. It will make you feel naked and exposed at first but, as you stay with this, you will learn that truth needs no clothing.

As you follow the path to your inner morality, many confused emotions may come to the surface of your everyday mind, causing you self-doubt and fear. You may feel worry that you are inferior to your colleagues and peers. Remember: you are not bad. You are essentially good, and intrinsically enlightened. You lack nothing. If you can accept this, the path will start to reveal itself.

Simply look at the natural world. Bees and flowers, clouds and rain, sun and moon, light and dark, birth and death, all of these are part of the continual cycle of truth. See how the ants and birds work together, each giving support to their own kind. Human beings often fail to do so. The seeds within the fruit only know one thing: that they must grow, blossom and bear fruit. Essentially, we human beings must do the same, but some of us have forgotten. The truth is everywhere, in all things, in all situations and is behind the beginning and comple-tion of everything. It can lead you to your spiritual potential and, most of all, it can reveal to you how to live your own life.

Remember, living in a way that is as true to yourself as you can be is not always an easy path. Do not climb spiritual mountains just because they are there, or seek the meaning of life because you feel you should. Life has only the meaning you give to it. The truth reveals life as it is.

The first one hundred years of the new millennium upon which we have just embarked will dictate the cycles and patterns for the future. New forms of emerging spiritual wisdom and consciousness are finding their roots. New technologies and the changes in the global money supply and the use of natural resources will all influence the evolution of human beings as a species.

In this 21st century, Tibetan wisdom teaches that the foundations of this new wisdom will be manifested in the rising up of female and feminine consciousness, influencing both the world view and individual development. This feminine consciousness will create new ways of thought, new insights into human nature and will become humanity's next step on the evolutionary path to the understanding of its own spiritual potential.

It can and will empower both men and women, giving new foundations to the notions of individual responsibility and revising our priorities in the way we live. Individual and social spirituality is going to be the only important human resource that will guide us to the understanding of ourselves and our planet. People all over the world are starting to understand, deep within themselves, that the so-called 'modern world' has not delivered. Although science and technology and rational philosophies have contributed to material and intellectual well-being, our spiritual needs are not being met.

Our inner wisdom and higher states of consciousness are the only bedrock of individual spiritual happiness. They are the resonance of the higher humanity that links all people in our species. But we feel separated from them. In this troubled time, careful understanding of the past, present and future can bring great insight.

Many people understand that our planet is simply a transition to a higher level. But often we have closed down those very perceptions that can reveal to us our inner light, and so we stay confined to this world and to its material emanations. The risk is that if we do not reach out now for whatever we see as heaven and higher consciousness, then hell and hellish states of mind will slowly creep upon us.

Our earth is going through a painful adolescence, for not only is humanity a young species but so also is the rock on which we live. We are living in a kind of global puberty. Squeezed between the old and the new, we forget the constant that is there regardless of history, calendars or politics: that is our ability both as individuals and as a species to reconnect with each other and with the gifts of nature. For this we need to allow our humility to emerge. Humility is the foundation of generosity.

Finding this humility comes by encouraging simplicity of thought and directness of action in all parts of your life. Respect the society that you find yourself in and understand that great value can be found in what you have and are. Anyone can understand and experience their spiritual potential without years of a particular training. A focused and sincere heart and a direct mental focus are often enough. The purpose is simply to comprehend the underlying spiritual nature of all things. From this develops a way of manifesting freedom, peace, happiness and consciousness.

<~>

All of us are wise. All of us have access to inner truth. No one holds a single key to truth above all others. Rest in your emerging divinity and consciousness. Do not grasp for it. Receive it and enjoy.

<~>

Live every day not as if it were your last, or as if you never lived before, but for what is: an unknown experience, potentially able to offer you a connection to your humanity and happiness. We need to realise that the process of travelling towards our dreams is in itself a spiritual experience.

In the next chapter you will discover how to create your soul for this life, a process the Tibetan Bön tradition called 'Activating Your Thunder', because the individual who has made their soul has the power of thunder and lightning to cut through ignorance and reveal truth to others.

CHAPTER TWO

Activating Your Thunder – how to make your soul and keep it

The soul is not eternal. A soul lasts for a lifetime and through the process of dying. Then it breaks down — a spiritually biodegradable process of the mind. So we are not reborn complete with a soul, but we do come to this life with all the ingredients to make one.

Each of us is a being with many dimensions, all working together simultaneously. As we start to explore these inner dimensions, in the process of building our souls for this life, we begin to know a little of the vastness and complexity of our consciousness. The soul is a device that holds and directs our potential consciousness and enlightenment. Regardless of our backgrounds, each of us is a beginner when it comes to building one. It's important to remember that there is no examination to be passed, no title to be gained, no point of perfection to be attained. The process is an experience that comes from understanding the energy within ourselves and all things.

Let me just clear up one common area of confusion. We are never completely what we imagine ourselves to be — either good or bad. This is because our view of our selves and our lives is made up, in the main, of the reactive emotions that I mentioned in Chapter 1. These ego-centric feelings, generated in the battle of everyday living, often go round and round on a psychic loop tape, replaying the same experiences within us. We may become addicted to a particular facet of an emotion that makes us feel good in some way. Don't get me wrong: emotions are important and valuable, but at the same time we should not let them fool us into believing that they are life or consciousness.

Most of what we consider to be our identity is the shadows of past habits and sensory overload. By starting to understand the nature of our habits, which form the everyday mind, we begin to be able to unite all these separate inner forces on the first step to creating our soul. It is then that we gain a vision of who we really are.

Love is essential to our humanity and thus to our souls. Love is experienced by people and living creatures as a means of understanding the nature of existence and the transient nature of possessions – people or objects – and suffering, as well as the unalterable process of karma.

Tibetan thought reminds us to show real care, love and compassion in all that we do and think to the best of our ability and intellect. Love for ourselves and others – in any context, experience or form – passionately involves itself in every living being, holding all things within its own calm cradle of respect and non-judgement. True love always wants the best for every creature in existence, loving all the world without prejudice, but with wisdom.

Non-attachment is an aspect of loving wisely, and involves being joyful in the joy of others. In simple terms, it means no-strings-attached love, without expectation or obligation. Love is often interwoven with some form of attachment, but in Tibetan thought, this is firmly discouraged. Attachment has connotations of expectation, need and even greed. When you love without attachments, you do so selflessly, without any expectation of reward. You simply love.

In Tibetan teachings you do not reject the world, you embrace it. You become intimate with life. The single acceptable and healthy type of attachment comes into this, and involves attachment to your own inner devotion and development. Attachment to the divine in yourself can inspire a real human love for everyone, which is truly remarkable. Consider how many people you love and are attached to: friends, loved ones and to enemies; teachers, parents, neighbours and co-workers; celebrities of all kinds and not least to your pets. The list goes on and on. Ask yourself, 'What is the nature of my attachment?' Many of these relationships can be positive tools for transformation, although they may also carry some threads of expectation and obligation that you might want to unravel.

Additionally, we need also to look at the attachment we have to our physical bodies. We may have a love affair with them or feel trapped in them, hate them or be anxious about them. We must learn to let go of any negative feelings with kindness, so we can relate to our bodies in a new and loving way. Similarly, we must learn to look beyond the concept that our bodies are our identities.

Whenever our capacity for love is great, so is our capacity for suffering. Through suffering we learn the timeless value of love. When we lose someone we care for through separation or death, we grieve and suffer, but from that attachment comes knowledge. If we value the emotion, the experience and attachment so that we can truly grieve, we can learn and move on. It is better to accept suffering in totality, than the prejudice-creating concept of inhuman composure.

Spirituality of any type should bring you closer to your humanity. If you end up cold and cut off, without emotional understanding, you have through your perception of holiness, committed an act of spiritual terrorism to both yourself and other people. The further we remove ourselves from others the more we are lost. The more detached we become from our humanity, the more powerful our egos become. Be human first, middle and last. That is where divinity is to be found.

This process of soul-making is creation of the highest type because we become the creators of our connection to a greater reality. It is vital that we learn to build a strong soul which can withstand the storms of everyday living.

In this chapter we will learn about the nature of consciousness, the physical and mental vitality we need to start building a soul, the five spiritual foundations of the soul, and how to develop our five senses.

This is the story of how I started to create my soul.

<~>

It was a summer's evening on Pihanga Mountain in the centre of the North Island of New Zealand.

The evening sky stood bright and strong against the night. Everything was still; there was no wind, no breeze. The lake below was placid, reflective. The mountain above stood strong, defiant and knowing.

'Tonight we shall start learning to make a soul,' said Ürgyen my teacher. 'We are all born without a soul, but most people do not know how to create one. You must first look at the energy of the soul. Observe.'

He gazed out across the valley. Everything became even more still than before. He raised his right hand into the air, his palm facing out into the night. He started to chant, slow and long, and everything in front of me burst into light and clear flame. My jaw hit my knees; a part of me could not believe what I saw. But my doubt faded as I looked closer: the sky, the stars, the trees, the air, mountain, lake and the hill I was on had become an incandescent flame. Then I looked down at myself: I too was part of this flame.

'This is the energy from which all things are made,' said Ürgyen. 'It is consciousness. It is you and I, and all living creatures. It is this energy that forms our minds and our souls.'

Suddenly it was gone. The stars, the mountain and the lake were as they were before.

<~>

My teacher explained that our senses are devices that interpret what is going on *around* us in the everyday world. Less obviously, they also interpret what is going on *within* us in the everyday world. Crucially, it is this spiritual dimension to our senses that allows our minds to connect with the energy that pulses in the hearts of other living creatures and in the essence of inanimate existence, from grains of sand on the seashore to vast oceans. You will learn the importance of interconnectedness in this chapter and at the end you will find exercises to help you develop your senses.

Every living thing is connected. Human beings, for instance, live in each other's consciousness more intimately than most people care to acknowledge. The main factors that influence and transform our senses and which we can use in building a soul are set out in this ancient Tibetan Bön saying:

<~>

> *Thought is the body of Sound.*
> *Sound is the body of Light.*
> *Light is the body of Consciousness.*
> *Consciousness is the body of humanity.*
> *The soul, once made, is the body of these.*

<~>

THOUGHT AND SOUND

Our thoughts are our individual distillation of the sounds of the world and the universe – of mankind, nature, of life living itself. These sounds fill the broad spectrum of life and find their expression in human thought, which then leads to creativity and endeavour.

SOUND AND LIGHT

According to ancient Tibetan beliefs, sound is made up of light. Light, both physical and spiritual, is the essence of the construction of any sound.

The entwining of sound and light are apparent in music, perhaps the most powerful and universal form of art. Inner light can drive forward sounds that form part of our personal environment, and the opposite is also true. From a Tibetan view, the music to which we are attracted actually creates light within our brains and nervous system, as well as encouraging spiritual light to shine within our consciousness.

Music, as well as other forms of art, is often an expression of the mental forces of humanity at any given time, as well as a reflection of the psychic health of our planet. This is because the works are full of light and sound – in other words, consciousness. Think of composers such as Mozart, Beethoven and Bach, and painters like Picasso and Matisse.

However dramatic they may seem at the time, shifts and changes in our world, as a result of wars, natural disasters and disease, and even pornography and pop music, are a natural part of the cycles of our planet as it floats in the universe.

LIGHT AND CONSCIOUSNESS

The essence of light is consciousness, whether it's physical energy – from the sun, the moon, a fire, even a light bulb – or inner spiritual energy. This consciousness is the summation of all physical and spiritual energies coming together. When you have made your soul, you will gain insight into the interrelationships between what people separate as spiritual or physical. You will understand that, in fact, they are the same energy expressed in different forms. When you truly accept this, you will find that the world gladly reveals itself in all its dimensions of existence.

CONSCIOUSNESS

Consciousness is our essence. It is the energy that creates everything in the universe.

Consciousness expresses itself in different ways. Our evolution as a physical species is wrapped around this consciousness. Think of the words 'spiritual', 'spirit' and 'inspiration', and compare them to the process that keeps our physical bodies alive – respiration. At its most fundamental, every breath we take is a physical expression of consciousness. Later in the book you will find some breathing exercises.

Consciousness does not change, neither does it stand still. It is the root of evolution. In very old Bön texts, it talks of a time millions of years ago when the world was young and covered in great cycles of floods. People lived in caves or on high mountains, yet they had the same consciousness as we do today. But the underlying consciousness, which exists in all things, is always slowly finding ways of evolving into broader and more profound dimensions. Without this process, we would not, for instance, be able to study our emotions, intellect and spirituality. The evolution of consciousness is why anyone can make a soul.

It is by creating the soul that you go from becoming reactive and controlled by both your emotional and physical environments into a state of consciousness when you become the originator of your life, understanding the flux and flow of consciousness and aware of knowing how to use it.

Now let us look at the cultural background in Tibetan teaching that helped develop the spiritual and psychological techniques of making a soul.

ORIGINS

As you know from the last chapter, Tibetan culture and spirituality originated in the shamanism of Central and Northern Asia. These cultures taught sophisticated theories of the mind, spiritual meditations and other techniques that connected the individual to a transcendent joy and a natural happiness.

A happy spiritual life was seen as a balance of spiritual and material activities. The first step was that you, as an individual, had to become empowered by making and keeping your soul. This meant that your life force, mental clarity and overall inner state must be stronger than the world around you. This included both the worlds of thoughts and emotions as well as the material world and the environment.

Then and now

Tibetan shamans (Ngagpas), like those from other cultures, sought to create a balance between humankind and the forces of nature. Nature in all its manifestations was deeply respected as the organ of the health of our planet by Ngagpas. With today's global environmental crisis and the new types of illnesses and diseases affecting the global community, it is crucial for all human beings to rediscover the relationships and harmonies central to shamanistic wisdom. In this way, the earth can be healed, repaired and managed, and humankind can be saved from global negativity, social decline and individual suffering. If we keep polluting our planet, we end up polluting ourselves, emotionally, physically and eventually spiritually.

If we develop a direct knowledge of our human consciousness and use it skilfully as we interact with all dimensions of life, we can achieve power and balance in our own lives and harmony for the earth.

BUILDING BLOCKS OF THE GODS

Ngagpas experience the divine essence in humanity on a daily basis. This can be true for each of us, but we are not consciously aware of it. We are all made from the building blocks of gods and it is in our power to find the optimum situations for happiness and spiritual awakening.

The Ngagpas' role within the world is to restore the natural harmonies that existed at the very first heartbeat of all humanity. Ngagpas create wise connections between all forms of consciousness, the forces of the natural world, those of the cosmos and other realms, and those of the earth in all its forms and variations.

This role is something that all human beings instinctually know and respond to. If we deny it, we deny ourselves. We are all Ngagpas in some way, within the personal context of our own lives. These skills come from discipline of the mind and body but they also derive from, and are grown by, the conscious creation and construction of a soul.

Soul energy and the creation of vitality

According to Tibetan wisdom, making a soul is dependent on having vitality. This is the life force that feeds us and gives us drive. The storehouse of vitality is created during our conception and activated during the physical birth event. It is crucial to the health of our bodies and minds; indeed, to our very existence as emotional, energetic and spiritual beings.

But this vital energy can become depleted by the ups and downs of life, and may be unable to renew itself. When this happens, illness, suffering, unhappiness, bad fortune or severe obstructions come into our lives and the creation of a soul seems an irrelevant concept.

Depleted vitality tries to renew itself, but the process may become distorted and result in the creation of obstructions and problems that come back again and again, just as you think you have finally dealt with them. This stems from a lack of the strong vitality that could bring them to a successful conclusion.

It may be difficult to restore strong vitality, but it can be done. Knowing more about your own personal history is the first step in restoring dwindling vitality. Think about the low points in your life and study, for example, what time of year they happened, what kinds of people were around you at the time and what those people meant to you. You will discover that there are cycles in your life, highs and lows that correspond to the rise and fall of your vitality. Often, because our vitality is unstable and fragile, we have very fast rises and falls, which are preludes to a series of repetitive problems, situations and obstructions. Examining these cycles will help you to understand the nature of your depleted vitality and how it happened.

The aim is not to create more vitality – you are born with a finite amount – but to improve the quality of your vital force, making it stronger and more durable. Treating yourself with respect and balance improves and restores vitality, facilitates the flow of happiness and good fortune, and enables you to set about the process of making a soul.

VITALITY AND THE ART OF LIVING WELL

It's important to remember that living well is not only a skill but an art, which involves three main factors: other people, your self and vitality. If you wish to practise the art then you must understand its components. Ancient Tibetan tradition teaches that there are nine types of activities, all of which are intimately connected with our physical, emotional and psychological states of vitality.

The nine types of vital activity concern:
1. Food and diet
2. Behaviour
3. Work/career
4. Our inner world
5. Spiritual needs and beliefs

6. Generosity and compassion
7. Mental discipline
8. Happiness
9. Sharing, giving and receiving

In the chapters that follow, you will find detailed information about these vital activities and how you can best nourish them. For now, here is a brief introduction to what they are and how they affect your life.

1. FOOD AND DIET

Food is energy and it gives better or lesser types of vitality to your system, depending on how you use it. Tibetan medicine is not just concerned with eating 'healthy' food, but with eating the right types of food for your physical and psychological type. If you eat foods that are not compatible with your body and psychological type, your vitality becomes dispersed and weak.

Now let us take a brief look at dieting. The Western world has gone diet mad. Dieting can be good for you, but if done incorrectly it damages your health and weakens your psychological and physical vitality in a very powerful way. When you start to diet, you change the way your body and mind works through the subtle restrictions you exercise on your attitudes and ideas, including the merit of different foodstuffs, your physical reaction to different foods and your body image.

Restricting what you eat is only of real benefit if you are ill. If you diet just to lose weight, the weight will return in some form. For dieting to be beneficial in the long term, there must be lifestyle changes that empower both your body and your mind. A sensible diet is a good way of fine-tuning the overall health of your body. A good diet should be undertaken for one month once every two years, in early to mid-January, to improve the vitality of your body and mind for the coming year.

Alcohol is an ancient and socially accepted drug so its abuse is very easy. It is good to reduce your alcohol intake to a level where it brings you occasional pleasure rather than constant remorse. If you drink a lot you deplete your vitality. Coffee can act in a similar way if it is abused. Like alcohol, caffeine is a complex drug whose abuse has created global social problems, particularly with the proliferation of caffeinated drinks. Drinking more water is wise for everyone, but is particularly important to counterbalance the effects of these drinks. The Tibetan approach to food and drink is outlined fully in Chapter 8.

2. BEHAVIOUR

This concerns the way you react to others and to circumstances. All human beings, regardless of how they may seem, are intrinsically fragile. The older we become, the more fragile we get.

One of the most important aspects of behaviour is speech and the thoughts behind it. Negative thoughts and speech diminish vitality and so diminish us. If you react in an unloving way to people you transfer your difficulties to them. Behaving in this way can easily become a habit and cause suffering both to you and to the people with whom you communicate. By learning how your mind works and reacts on a day-to-day basis (what I call your 'everyday mind'), you will learn not to harm either your own fragile emotional and physical state, or that of anyone else.

If you get a bad reaction from someone, you invariably pass it on. This is where the majority of people cause themselves and others most pain, which decreases their vitality. This happens because deep within every human being is an honest and heartfelt desire to communicate and to interact in a friendly and kind way with others. When we are treated 'badly', as we see it, we feel let down and abused. So our aim is to become unaffected by rejection, rudeness or unkindness, and to help others to achieve the same immunity.

Vitality has a personality of its own, which seeks to expand and blend with everything, from rocks and stars to people and animals. Though it may not be obvious to us, it is this impulse that impels us to seek communication with each other, to be creative, to aspire to the highest dimensions of human intelligence. Misused, however, this impulse can be gruesome and evil, seeking dominion over others.

3. WORK AND CAREER

Work is any activity that involves people communicating with each other, so it is a vast part of human life. In these situations, there is always an exchange of vitality between people, and it is a natural process. According to Tibetan wisdom, the essential reason for all human work is to interact with others and to experience a heightened vitality. This experience in turn creates the work and its end result.

Often in the workplace or in your career, however, you will experience fatigue, tiredness and a loss of vitality. This comes not from the activity, but how you react to it, and also from the way you communicate with others and they with you. Tibetan teaching has always suggested that in any form of human activity or endeavour you achieve your aims with other people helping you. But we need to be watchful because while some people can increase or stabilise your vitality, others can reduce it.

You need to recognise when your vitality is being abused, either consciously or unconsciously. Conversely, if you feel empowered by other people, you need to work out how you can best handle it. Vital force is an intimate aspect of our individuality within the everyday world and it is our personal responsibility to look after it.

Our attitude to work is key. Many people think of it as a means to pay for our lives – that work is something we have to do in order to make money or be part of society. This is partly true, of course, but if you work with this attitude in mind, your vitality will certainly diminish. Also the workplace we choose and/or the career ambitions we set for ourselves are often highly effective devices for reducing the potency of our vitality, or even cutting us off from our connection to it.

Constructive attitudes to work can build up your vitality. Anything you do can be perceived as a way for your consciousness to learn new life experiences. Work shows us our limitations but also our qualities and talents. It can make us more emotionally mature, which allows us to become less affected by negative work environments or unskilful people.

Yes, many places of work are negative. You may be stabbed in the back, for instance, or simply be stuck in a mediocre organisation. Remember that the workplace is often where we discover the nature of karmic forces, for human nature is shown there in all its guises. By overcoming such problems we are able to connect with our own inner vitality. Remember, too, that organisations, workplaces and your own career have their own special vital force which you will begin to recognise as you make contact with your own vitality.

Lastly, if you find you cannot practice your spiritual beliefs in the workplace, you must revisit what you believe, because that area of your vitality is weak.

4. INNER WORLD

Your inner world is a place of secrets, dreams, hopes, aspirations, fantasies and plans – of longing, anger, love, hope, ambition and the yearning for happiness. This inner place can be both a sanctuary and a place of turmoil. It is where vitality withers or flourishes because here we create our deepest identity through our desires. Your vitality takes on the qualities of the dominant emotional forces that are active deep within you. These are the true forces that feed our everyday persona.

Vitality is intrinsically pure, all encompassing and life giving. But we can pollute it by repeated unskilful actions and thoughts, such as abusing our bodies through drugs or other unskilful behaviour that cause us and other people hurt, pain or confusion. So each of us needs to be aware of the nature of our inner world. Is it really the place you want to be? Are you happy there?

Our inner world sets up the way in which we relate to the world around us. It guides us to all of the achievements and success in our lives. It is the inner world that decides our needs and desires as they really take place, because our inner world is who we really are.

Without an inner world that functions in an integrated way, we do not have a life, simply an experience of living spattered by periods of unknowing, powerlessness and the sudden need for control. When life seems more powerful than you do, your inner world needs healing.

Nearly all of us pass our lives floating on top of our inner world, sublimely unconscious of just how unknowing and how lacking in personal empowerment we really are. Yet if we have the courage to explore within, we will discover among the fear and anger an endless beauty, an eternal light that shines from within us out into a world and universe of endless possibilities. At the core of our inner world beats an endless love that needs no language or intelligence to be understood, just a heart that is ready to be humble.

5. SPIRITUAL NEEDS AND BELIEFS

A spiritual belief is quite different from a spiritual need. A spiritual belief enables you to understand a truth in your own way. A spiritual need enables you to live, to be alive. Needs are basic and instinctual, the staple diet of the consciousness that makes us human. Each of us has spiritual needs that are determined by the way that we have lived since conception. If, as individuals, we do not find a way to fulfil these needs, our lives are incomplete and we become ill.

Spiritual needs fall into three basic groups:

1. The need for a reality of belonging, safety and harmony.
2. The need for a reality of happiness, beauty and achievement.
3. The need for a reality of continuity, wisdom and unconditional love.

In this new millennium, people have needs, not beliefs. Because this new century is the template for those to come, people are and will continue to be under increasing psychic pressure. The way in which this pressure can be released is through the fulfilment of spiritual need. The vitality that comes from this is the anchor of all of the nine activities.

The vitality of spiritual need unites all living creatures in a common inheritance of life and living. By cultivating it through self-knowledge, you become more human; that is, you become connected to the divinity that exists in the daily experience of living. By knowing the beauty that upholds the functions of every day life, you will discover that ordinary events and situations hold the key to experiencing your spiritual beauty and perfection.

In the search for self-knowledge, the greatest adventure that any person can undertake is the voyage within. You do not need to look outside your life to find greater truths because every day of your life is an enormous state of grace that holds lessons about your true nature. Spiritual development is just like living and the act of dying; no one can prepare you for the process, you learn as you go along. All you need is the courage to start.

The one thing that everyone needs on their spiritual journey is the quality of acceptance. This is the greatest survival tool of all, a spiritual Swiss army knife, because it teaches you adaptability, patience and good humour. These three qualities make your life enjoyable, give perspective in all your experiences, and help you to assess and treasure your vitality.

6. GENEROSITY AND COMPASSION

Generosity and compassion are the two structures of life that hold it together. They are the underpinning of all good things. Without them our lives have no vitality; they are merely shadows, sick, empty and one-dimensional.

Generosity is not just the act or mental attitude of giving, it is also a way of living that creates abundance for everyone else. Generosity is life-giving.

Compassion, however, is life-making. It is a transformational state of consciousness that gives new life to all living beings who consider themselves defeated by the events of their lives.

Compassion is the foundation and identity of humanity. By showing compassion as best we can, we become more evolved and more integrated. This creates an enduring wisdom, the nature of which is generosity of spirit. This in turn becomes happiness.

7. MENTAL DISCIPLINE

Mental discipline is the first step in experiencing lasting happiness. You need mental discipline to understand and appreciate your happiness. When people are happy but do not understand why, they often misuse their happiness. Then vitality is diminished and happiness cannot be supported. So it vanishes.

If we know why and how we are happy we can create more happiness for ourselves, and that means more vitality. This is the start of mental discipline. Mental discipline is not a strict regimented control of the way in which your mind deals with facts by routine or planned structure; it is a state of wisdom.

This wisdom does not come from knowledge or intellect – factual information is memory not wisdom – but from an openness that expands your emotional and spiritual awareness. Ignorance is generated when your mind is closed or will not accept new influences in your life.

The wiser a person becomes, the freer they are from anger, delusion, hatred, possessiveness and all forms of prejudice. They become totally receptive to all offerings from life. They are receptive but also discerning.

There is a danger of creating a false mental discipline through being absorbed by religion rather than spirituality. It is here that we should explore a little more the nature of the senses. We must learn to value our senses and the experiences they bring to us. We must respect them so their gifts can grow in intensity and depth. From this they become clear and shine with the light that streams out of total realisation.

Our senses allow our inner essence to unfold and from this comes originality, beauty and the sparks of perception. Colours, sounds, smells, touch, tastes and all physical sensations connect us all to each other's experience of humanity. This connection is the way to unity, to understanding that each human being on the planet today is a link to the experience of enlightenment. As we discover this, a spiritual echo starts to vibrate on a frequency within our inner minds that excites us to search for meaning.

But if we do not go through this process for ourselves and only pick up the echo, we construct a religion rather than creating a spiritual experience. Religion alone is a false mental discipline that can become rigid and unbending. Both in history and the world today there are many examples of religious intolerance, violence and corruption created out of false mental discipline.

True mental discipline is free of ego. It is not a denial of who you are, but an understanding of how your mind works, how it supports you – and how it tricks you. The more you can discipline and direct your mental forces, the better quality of mental experience you will have. It will create wisdom and generate awareness and a happiness that survives within you regardless of what happens in your daily life.

We have discussed happiness a lot in previous sections because it is so important. Most people equate happiness with an obvious absence of suffering. This is not happiness, but a lack of problems. Often, however, we do not believe that there is a deeper happiness.

A deeper happiness does exist, if we take the trouble to cultivate it. We can grow happiness inside us. Just like food crops, true happiness must be planted from seed, grown, harvested and made into a useful creation. Cultivating this particular vitality is one of the foundations of why each of us has a human existence. People who have the vitality of happiness bring happiness to all living creatures just by the very fact that they exist. Happiness is the greatest form of beauty that we can experience.

Happiness also keeps us healthy. If a patient consults a physician of Tibetan medicine about a lack of vitality, the first thing he or she will do is to discover if the person is happy or not, and why. When just one person is unhappy, all of humankind becomes affected in lesser or greater ways. With today's global media, we know that millions of people are very unhappy every day and this affects us.

Our perception of happiness and suffering is sometimes ill-founded. If you have ever dealt with people who experience ongoing suffering year in, year out, you will know that under the fatigue lives a beauty and a happiness. They know that suffering does not go on forever. They know, too, that however you are feeling, happiness can come at any time and embrace you, rekindling your humanity. I have seen it happen in war zones and in the sick beds of the First World. It is something we should not forget.

The erratic vitality of our human species has caused a deep lack of communal vitality across the world, which has resulted in hunger, war, famine, disease and climate change. If we were able to restore the vital force of loving kindness to the world, the collective burden that we unconsciously share would start to lift. Our mental and emotional faculties would become transformed. It would take some considerable time, but each of us can start to contribute a little by knowing ourselves. As our vitality grows, the terrible situations that millions of people experience will start to improve.

Suffering takes on many forms and has much to teach us. When we consider other people's experiences, we know that happiness is never far from us. It is everywhere, in all things. It bubbles under the surface of our daily lives waiting for us to recognise it in ourselves.

9. SHARING, RECEIVING AND GIVING

These three activities can determine the outcome of our own personal humanity. Yet we tend to forget them as a form of communication because they take place every minute of our daily lives. How much we give, receive and share determines our abilities to understand ourselves.

The vitality generated by giving without expectations helps to heal the mind of agitation and encourages physical health both in the giver and the receiver. Sharing skilfully acknowledges that we are all caretakers of what we have or own, and that resources – great or small – are to be enjoyed but also respected, ready to pass on to new caretakers. Receiving is the hardest aspect of this vitality. To receive well means a state of humility where we can accept the individual who gives something to our consciousness. We also need to be able to distinguish when this is beneficial to us and when it is not advisable.

The art of skilful receiving generates currents of positive energy that flow throughout the world, creating generosity, material abundance, and cultural and scientific progress. We are all involved in the generation of these good things, so each one of us is responsible for all aspects of the planet in which we live, as caretakers and guides to its evolution.

As well as being caretakers for the planet, we are caretakers and guides for ourselves. This means that we need to treat ourselves with more generosity through giving, sharing and most importantly, receiving human kindness. There is no greater experience in any person's life than to be treated with genuine human kindness. It is an act of grace that transforms us all and that all of us are able to share in. Beneath the masks of everyday living, this state of grace is who we really are.

THE FIVE FOUNDATIONS OF THE SOUL

Just as your house needs foundations, so too does your soul. The bricks and mortar of the soul are five forms of intelligence that you can integrate into your daily life to form your spiritual energy and power.

The first foundation is experiencing the knowing behind your senses.

The second foundation is experiencing inner silence.

The third foundation is learning to listen.

The fourth foundation is understanding the nature of free will and the interconnection between all things.

The fifth foundation is accepting that consciousness is in everyone and everything.

The benefits of building these foundations are immense. They are traditionally regarded as five aspects of our consciousness that become developed as we create our soul potential. You will find these benefits explained below, following the descriptions of the foundations. I have described my own experiences of learning some of the five foundations because it is the simplest way to explain.

<~>

The world made by human beings often demands a great deal from each of us. These demands can cause us to treat our lives without much respect. This is the nature of unconnected living. The universe, the natural world, our inner consciousness make no such demands. The inner world, the natural world and the universe make only one request and there is plenty of time to hear it.

The request is this: You are already in a state of grace and balance. You are already awake to the potential of your consciousness. Please accept this as so and it shall take place.

Listen. All of this is closer than you think. Enlightenment is already blazing within you. It does not matter who you are or what you have done. Be humble enough to love yourself and then you can move forward.

<~>

The first foundation: experiencing the knowing behind your senses

My breathing was heavy and my lungs felt as if they were being beaten by a sledgehammer. My heart banged loud in my head. Thunder from the nearby mountain yelled defiance across the valley, lightning streaked across the peaks. Then everything stopped.

Silence.

Then the absence of silence.

A blue flickering light ran through me. It burned to white. The white turned to the sound of the ocean. A gentle humming started in my physical heart, then started to move in a spiral throughout my body. Each note was a little pearl of sound. Each pearl was connected to the next on a thread. The thread was me, formed of my burnt desires and fearfulness, of wonder and discipline, of divinity and consciousness.

The making of my soul had begun.

The spiral stretched through all my bones, moving into the sacred part of my brain where, according to Tibetan beliefs, the potential for soul-making slept. The world around me was me. As the wind blew, so did I. As a stranger died, so did I. And I knew that there were no strangers in our lives, only distant relatives to whom we have not yet been introduced.

I could feel the structures of my mind link with my body. My nervous system was my thinking process, which became a fuse of burning consciousness, like a flaming beacon in a desert. Within me I saw the inner tree, the burning bush described by the Ngagpas.

The tree was the vital channels of the mental body joining with the physical to create the soul. My senses started to transform. Each one became a form of intelligence, all five working together to hold my consciousness, to form my spiritual energy and power.

BENEFITS: MATERIAL

As you develop this energy, you will find that problems concerning money, relationships, career and health start to improve. You will begin to learn about the nature of material energy and the most auspicious times in which to create financial and material success. You will begin to understand the essential nature of the relationships around you. You will either want to start a new, more fulfilling career, or reappraise your current job or occupation. You will begin to recognise how all of these activities affect your physical and mental health and this will help you to improve the types of vitality that help you.

The second foundation: experiencing inner silence

Ürgyen gazed at the fire, drinking tea. Everything was filled with the roar of divinity. But there was silence. No wind. No crackling fire, no loud thoughts, no thunder on the mountain.

I knew I was looking into the world of the everyday mind through the eyes of my new soul. Then, with a roar of nature, it all returned: the wind blew, the fire crackled, thunder crashed around the mountain.

Ürgyen looked up. 'The second foundation of building a soul is to be in the silence.'

Across the valley on the mountain came a peal of thunder and a flash of sheet lightning. The full moon hung over the mountain peak, watching.

Silence is a process not a sound. It is something we must work to understand. Silence is an important faculty of human consciousness. Silence allows our consciousness to expand, and all the rubbish of our minds and personality to fall away, so we can see ourselves a little more clearly. It reveals to us whether we like our own company or not.

The more time we spend in the company of silence the more we are able to understand the mental and physical structures for inner change. To grow we need to be unafraid of silence. If we regard it only as the absence of noise, it can be overwhelming. Silence is the still point within all sound and motion. Just as a tornado has a still centre, so silence is at the centre of all things. The more we understand silence, the more we know about listening, about speech and about thought. Silence is seen as the first step to thinking well.

Like most things in our lives, silence must be experienced to be understood. Most of us have very little silence in our lives, because our minds are too busy banging away at everyday affairs to stop and experience silence. You cannot be silent but silence can be within you.

If you discover the silence within, your life will change. You will want something else, something more fulfilling. Possibly your current lifestyle will taste stale and outmoded. Alternatively, it could suddenly become more enriched and improve beyond recognition.

Fulfilment is not truth or happiness. Fulfilment in this context means a completion of activities and emotions, the natural end to a process of understanding. Fulfilment can come to you by allowing the silence within to manifest itself.

BENEFITS: MENTAL AND EMOTIONAL

Your mental abilities will become more structured and comprehensive; you will be able to marry intuition with your everyday life to have a truly creative mental dimension. Problem-solving will become easier. Access to your intellectual skills will be easier and you will also understand the origins of your emotions. Understanding how our emotions work and how they form the instinctual part of us inspires us to treat our emotional personality with more respect.

The third foundation: learning to listen

Hearing and listening are very different activities. Hearing is instinctual, a process of active consciousness that enables each of us to comprehend the world around us and to understand what we are hearing. Hearing comes from the everyday mind.

Listening is a spiritual skill whereby you can become the same as whatever you are listening to, and know its essence. Listening activates the essential qualities of what is being listened to, whether that is a person or anything else. Listening goes beyond using your ears; all your other senses connect and become involved, too.

Listening with an open heart creates relaxation, good health and recognition of consciousness on both sides. Most of all, true listening is a mark of respect and compassion for whatever you listen to.

Listening is the key to the body's lock. Consciousness is the door that opens if you have learned how to listen well. Listen to the wisdom and energy of your body and you will know that, like the mind, the body moves in cycles that can guide you to transformation.

BENEFITS: INTELLECTUAL

Your intellectual capacities will start to improve and you will be able to grasp intellectual aspects of your own mind and apply them. The development of intellectual abilities is an important aspect of a balanced spiritual wisdom.

Intellect can be used to help you understand and achieve happiness. You can achieve happiness by using reason, logic, examination and discernment to observe the nature of how people suffer.

As you do this, you start to equate what you have seen with your experiences of suffering and those of other people. Because you are a human being, you are able to work out the cause of your suffering. This is a great ability, but one that many people do not use.

It is through your intellect that spiritual and emotional growth must express themselves so that you will then have an intellectual understanding of an inner experience that is mostly beyond words. Mental discipline is important here because it helps you to value what you have made.

The fourth foundation: understanding the nature of free will and the interconnection between all things

Because we are physically alive, emotionally active and spiritually aware, this foundation is an ongoing experience that is with us all our lives in differing forms of development.

It can be developed through many different means. Free will starts as a product of ignorance, but can become a tool of the wise. Free will originates because we often act in ignorance and do something – big or small, thought or deed – without knowing the consequences.

As we grow in consciousness, however, and know more about the possible interactions of thought, actions and events, our will becomes free in a different way, because it becomes more informed. At this juncture, we know our responsibilities to other living creatures and to our fellow human beings. Then it is up to us to decide to live as we choose.

There is an interconnection between all things. By simply trying to listen to it, appreciate it and understand it as much as you are able, you will attract its energy. That will support you and bring you to an experience that leads to the benefits explained below. Happiness comes from knowing of and experiencing the interconnection of all people on this planet. It comes from taking responsibility for creating our own happiness, then sharing that with others.

BENEFITS: EMOTIONAL

You will experience the dynamic nature of emotions and how they nurture and feed everything that makes us human, both as physical and spiritual beings. The origins of our emotional patterns, habits and desires, preferences and prejudices, all can be discovered and understood.

Emotional energy is the force that connects us to the cycles of nature and to other instinctual forces within humanity. By making a soul, you move beyond the limitations of instinct into the experience of empathy. Empathy is educated and disciplined intuitive energy of such refinement and loving power that you can identify with other people. They experience you doing so, which brings them hope and healing. Many people can do this in different ways. Perhaps you can. Try. In such things we are all novices because it is an experience that we must constantly relearn and re-experience.

Instinct is not bad, but it can be indulgent, because it is conditioned by the everyday mind. Empathy is the desire to connect with other people with unreserved compassion tempered by discernment. As people become empathetic because of their own life experiences and the inner exploration of their consciousness, they become less dominated by the negativities of instinct. As this happens, humanity as a whole will evolve. Our instinctual nature as a species will become more refined, less fearful and more intelligent. Instinct will reveal its positive qualities, showing each individual the dimensions of creativity that exist within everyone.

Human emotions drive us to spiritual insight. You start to understand that spirituality is not outside you and that while its nature is unique to each person there are common experiences that bind all people together. You will also know that you do not need to be in a rush in order to know who you are and can be.

The fifth foundation: accepting that consciousness is in everything and everyone

We are an insecure species, each of us locked in our own little world. The quest for security can trick us in different ways. For many people, our own worlds seem safe, whatever our personal circumstances. Even problems become a source of comfort, giving us a purpose and identity. From our small worlds we look out and judge others but often, in our rush to evaluate them, we are misled by appearances. We see the outer shell but overlook the inner beauty in everyone and everything, the essence that contains liberating consciousness. Of course, it may be well hidden, but if we develop the sensitivity to perceive it, it is always there.

This awareness of a greater reality allows a transformative impulse to kick in. The desire for spiritual awakening can disrupt your previous existence in a major way. It comes from the innermost core of our humanity where we are all aware of an inherent cosmic order. It allows us to move from an egocentric consciousness revolving around our intellect and emotions into a deeper universal consciousness, which leads us to a state of union with all life.

In this process, intellectual powers of reason, deduction and creation change from a one-dimensional experience into multi-dimensional tools of time, space and matter, emanating from the clear light of our highest being.

Each of us is a portal through which every aspect of energy within the universe may become aware of its own nature, a vibrant consciousness in search of itself. This energy is a frequency of such intensity that the universe can fashion itself as a human being, animal, plant, fish, rock or chewing gum stuck to the pavement in some big city. But it is never divorced from itself; it remains its own centre.

In this swirling cosmic consciousness, the reality that you and I inhabit day-to-day and the realities of our inner perceptions are always merged. This merging creates confusion: we must work within the sharp embrace of everyday reality but we also desire to experience pure universal energy. The confusion engenders a sense of separateness and a longing for meaning. We can, however, build a bridge between the two aspects of reality by infusing our desire for meaning with our own sense of the nature of consciousness. We should not force this, simply becoming aware of the potential will help.

BENEFITS: SPIRITUAL

In this aspect, you will start to unfold the higher dimensions of human consciousness and here you will experience the ways of integrating the everyday and the inner spiritual minds. The value of using spiritual insight in very practical ways — at work, say, or with your family, to explore your creativity or simply to clean your windows better — becomes self-evident because it makes you sane and balanced. There is no benefit in experiencing higher aspects of human consciousness if it leaves you unbalanced. The higher you move within the aspects of your consciousness the more you need to remember that. All spiritual experiences need strong foundations that can withstand the earthquakes of human consciousness as it moves towards a more profound recognition of itself.

TRANSFORMING THE FIVE SENSES

Each of the five senses that we take for granted on a daily basis is a pathway to making our soul. So they underpin the physical, emotional and mental structure which can enable us to find happiness, abundance, good fortune, health and wisdom.

The senses are intimately connected to the mind. Most people think that the mind is comprised of thoughts and feelings, memories and sensations. In fact, these are the debris of the brain. The mind is the vast flowing expanse of high material energy that percolates through all things physical in this world and the universe.

The mind glues everything together, but through this very process it can ensnare itself, sandwiched between walls of desire and undeveloped consciousness. Our minds stay trapped much of the time, but transforming your senses and using their abilities and functions can safely remove the fortifications. Liberated once more, your mind can connect with the larger mind energy of humanity.

We can learn to have direct experience of the spiritual universe by transforming our senses in a six-stage process called 'Chilu'. Firstly, here is a short explanation of the potential of each sense, that you will see reflects the five foundations of the soul, and their related benefits. When we experience our senses in a physical way, as most of us do, we have a limited sensory experience; but if we awaken them, through a special technique, which you will learn later, you will discover a particular type of consciousness for each sense and the colour associated with it.

SIGHT

The sense of sight is about perception, looking into the heart of things, knowing your inner truth and rediscovering your innocence and natural joyfulness. Transforming sight helps you to know what is behind your senses and what they are really for. Every sense is ruled by a colour and for sight, this is a pure white light. The mental aspect of consciousness is awakened by this sense and colour.

SMELL

Through the sense of smell you learn about silence and also how all things are connected and interdependent. Forgiveness and the ability to love unconditionally are linked with smell. A warm and happy yellow light influences this sense. The emotional aspect of consciousness is awakened by this sense and colour.

HEARING

Through your hearing, you can start to listen to your physical cycles and discover their wisdom and connections to inner energy. Hearing can help you to overcome fearfulness and see through illusion. A blood-red light, warm, permeating and life-giving, is linked to hearing. The intellectual aspect of consciousness is awakened by this sense and colour.

TOUCH

Through training your sense of touch you will discover the nature of impermanence and that true success and happiness only come about by living in accordance with what makes you happy. The power to overcome obstructions is gained by training this sense. You will also learn about the value of wealth, money and power, and the nature of the material world. A gentle green light is associated with touch. The material aspect of consciousness is awakened by this sense and colour.

TASTE

The sense of taste enables you to experience how consciousness, spirituality, goodness and happiness exist in everything, regardless of appearances or circumstances. A sky-blue light is connected with the sense of taste. The spiritual aspect of consciousness is awakened by this sense and colour.

 THE MIND TREE

The transformation of your senses is manifest in the creation of a network of energy pathways that lead from the senses through the body to the brain and allow you to experience the spiritual universe more directly. The ancient Tibetans called this the 'mind tree'. The roots are in the brain, and its branches, leaves, fruits and flowers are the five senses as they undergo the steps of transformation.

Step one

SIGHT

Sit comfortably with your eyes open. Instead of looking out through your eyes at the world, think that the world is flowing through your eyes, gathering at the roof of your mouth and then flowing down into the centre of your chest. As the world flows through you it changes slowly into a flow of pure sparkling white light. In your chest, it forms naturally into a sphere of vision and white light.

SMELL

Sit comfortably with your eyes closed and place your attention inside your nose. Feel your nose smelling. Let whatever you smell gather at the roof of your mouth, then flow down into the centre of your chest. As the smells flow through your body they transform into a beautiful yellow light. In your chest, it forms into a sphere of smell and yellow light, placing itself under the white sphere.

HEARING

Sit comfortably with your eyes closed and listen to all the sounds around you. Think of them flowing through your ears, into the roof of your mouth, gathering there, before flowing down into the centre of your chest. As these sounds move within you, they become a beautiful blood-red light flowing through you into your chest. There it gathers itself into a sphere of all that you have heard and the beautiful red light and places itself underneath the yellow sphere.

TOUCH

Sit comfortably with your eyes closed, hands together cupped. Place your mind into your hands, then let it expand into each of your finger-tips. Once you feel this, touch the atmosphere around you; allow it to flow into your fingertips, up through your arms and neck and into the roof of your mouth, where it gathers before flowing down into the centre of your chest. All that you touch in the atmosphere turns into a green light flowing from the atmosphere into you. In your chest, this forms into a sphere and places itself under the blood-red sphere.

TASTE

Sit comfortably with your eyes closed and your mouth gently open. Place all your attention into your tongue. Let all the atmosphere and environment around you flow into it. Allow all of your body to flow into the taste buds of your tongue. Let your body and the taste of the atmosphere and environment mix together where they gather at the roof of your mouth, and flow down into the centre of your chest. As they flow down they become a sky-blue light, and form a sphere of tastes and sky-blue light which places itself underneath the green sphere.

You should have a line of spheres with the colours in this order radiating with their own special brilliance:

- White
- Yellow
- Blood-red
- Green
- Sky-blue

When you have the spheres in order, start to breathe in and out slowly through your nose. As you do this, each of the spheres becomes sealed within you. Now you can move onto the next stage.

Step two

Practise step one for a few minutes daily for three weeks. Then you can go on to the second stage. The practice is the same as in stage one, but when the coloured spheres are placed in their order you do the following:

Working from the centre of your chest, put the white sphere to your top left, the yellow sphere to your top right, the blood-red sphere to your bottom left, the green sphere to your bottom right and the sky-blue sphere in the centre, like this:

White   *Yellow*

Sky-Blue

Blood-Red   *Green*

Then, mentally direct the white light to the yellow sphere, the yellow to the green sphere, the green to the blood-red sphere, and the blood-red to the white sphere.

Next direct light from the white sphere into the centre of the sky-blue sphere. Do the same with the yellow, the green and the blood-red spheres so that they are all connected. Take as long as you wish on this step, as there is no rush.

Steps one and two will begin to increase the acuteness of your senses: you will physically see, hear, touch, smell and taste more. Your overall health will improve as well as your everyday life. Often physical illnesses or continuing psychological problems can improve and are sometimes cured by this practice.

Step three

After some time in step two, you can start to practise the following. Focus on the sky-blue sphere and let it become one with your physical heart. Imagine a channel of sky-blue light moving from the combined sphere and heart moving slowly up into the back of your neck and head, then up into the central top area of your head. Then start to inhale from your heart to the top of your head; exhale from the top of your head out through your heart. Repeat step two.

Step four

In this step you are going to breathe in all the colours of the spheres at once, taking them up the channel from the heart, through the neck and the back of the head to the centre of your head. As you breathe in, draw them up gently without force. The colours will start to become intertwined like a rope of white, yellow, blood-red, green and sky-blue strands. As you exhale from the top of your head and out through your heart, the colours return to their appropriate spheres. Do this for some time until you feel ready to move onto step five.

Step five

Practise as step four up to the point where the coloured rope comes up to the centre top of your head. Then visualise all the colours cascading their brilliance over you, slowly and gently, like a waterfall of colours.

Your mind and body are awash with the flux and flow of these colours. Slowly, gently they subside, and the rope of intertwined colours hangs in space above your head. Breathe in and out gently through your nose. As you breathe, the coloured rope pulses with each in breath and out. At this point, imagine the rope transforming into an egg formed of all these intertwined colours, pulsing with beautiful light and the qualities of all your senses.

Gently and softly, but purposefully, sing the following sacred sounds. Each sound relates to a colour that influences one of your senses.

<~>

Sing a long A, so that the first sound is AAAAH, *the second* LARRRM.
'AH': *white light flashes within the egg (sight)*
'LAM': *yellow light flashes within the egg (smell)*
'BAM': *blood-red flashes within the egg (hearing)*
'RAM': *green light flashes within the egg (touch)*
'YAM': *sky-blue light flashes within the egg (taste)*

<~>

Wonderful feelings of purity and energy flow through your mind and body. You feel refreshed, strong and peaceful.

As you practise all the steps, you will find that the entire process becomes easy, effortless and pleasant. Then you can move on to the final stage, step six.

Step six

In this step you can start to harmonise and integrate your emotional, intellectual, physical and spiritual worlds by activating the lights and the egg. Simply go on doing the steps and send your thoughts to the light: they will create harmony in anything you do.

After a while you will find that you can leave the intertwined rope of colours and the egg permanently active above the centre of your head. The energy behind your thoughts, actions and emotions can be stored and empowered within the egg, thus increasing the quality and energy of your personality. This builds your soul.

The rope and the egg are indestructible as long as you have vitality. If you become ill, draw this energetic device back down into the spheres. This particular form of Chilu is safe, powerful and very relevant in today's world. It will empower anyone, bringing enhanced mental clarity and at the same time expanding and integrating consciousness into all aspects of your life. It heals stress and helps you to create stress-free actions. More importantly, it is a spiritual device that will bring happiness as you create deeper harmony in yourself. It can be used to help people overcome their fear of living as well as death and as a means to die well.

As you start to use this Chilu to develop your soul, do not strive to make it happen: allow it to find its own time to grow and develop. Remember that the reason why you or anyone can do this, and experience the results, is that within you is an innate goodness that seeks its way to full recognition and enlightenment. Your power, wisdom and discernment have awakened and, of course, your love for and of life, and your compassion for all that is. Remember it is only compassion that can make all that is into all that it can be. Deep in the essence of all things is compassion.

Consciousness rejoices in itself and this is compassion.

<~>

My senses pulsed with the light flowing through me. The world around me offered up new dimensions of awareness as my consciousness began to develop within the egg. I could feel and see this energetic rope of transformed senses flowing into the heart of the egg and my soul began to be formed in front of me.

The higher aspects of my consciousness merged with the lower, the skilful with the clumsy, the refined with the rough. My humanity began to dawn upon me and its light was as vast as the planet.

All my senses had become pathways of intelligence, an intelligence born from the essence of my mind and the foundations of my consciousness. It was a self-creating intelligence, existing in everything, everywhere.

I had not become perfect, enlightened or special. I had become more human.

Slowly I opened my eyes, breathed in the morning air and looked at the fire smoking gently. I gazed at the mountain, at the valley and the lake. I gazed at my teacher and felt profoundly normal.

'Tea?' he asked, offering me a cup. I took the cup, absorbing its fragrance. As I brought it to my lips and drank, the tea and I drank each other.

Fusion.

CHAPTER THREE
Karma Mechanics

*T*ibetan medicine teaches that illness is a language that communicates the interacting forces of the mind and body. This language is common throughout the world, but many of us have forgotten what the words mean. We can no longer understand our own illnesses, or those of others.

Tibetan physicians are taught that human beings are always ill in some way, no matter how we appear. This is because our lives on this planet are effectively the working-out of karma. Karma is the thread of invisible, intangible, all-pervading energy of which material life is woven. Karma is inescapable. It affects every living being all the time.

Enlightenment is the pure perfection that flows through moment to moment, millisecond to millisecond, in a continuous present where past and future are irrelevant concepts. Enlightenment is distinguished by the complete absence of egotism.

Compare that to our lives in this material world, where the past and present jostle to occupy the moment – where even the simplest action is complex, contingent on something or someone else. This is usually brought about by our perceived need to protect and promote ourselves.

Karma is the origin of all causes and conditions that shape our lives in this material world. From a Tibetan perspective, every event in our lives, big or little, creates another. We create patterns of energy and sow the seeds of further karma. Life well lived is a process of gaining the skills to understand that.

Karma is not romantic, spiritual or belonging to special people. It is the stuff of birth and death, suffering and health and of all physical life, both active and dormant. Our characters and desires evolve from our past actions and thoughts. How and what we think; what we do and don't do; good thoughts, deeds and habits, or bad ones; the way we see the world: 'I'm bored with everything', 'I hate my life', or the old favourite 'It's all your fault'. All of these are responses and reactions to karmic influences.

One woman likens the concept of karma to a vast cosmic jigsaw puzzle:

<~>

> *For five decades, my life had been up and down, good and bad, simple and complex. It was like a vast jigsaw puzzle but no one had given me the box with the picture on it. I could see thousands and millions of tiny pieces tumbling and wheeling. Sometimes a few would come down and seemingly become organised, then the chaos would begin again. My life seemed happy but under-neath it all, I had a suspicion everything might be pointless, including me. Taking the notion of karma on board gave me this most profound feeling that there is a big picture of my life even though I may never see it.*

<~>

Karma is the key to why we become ill, and illness itself is a direct way of understanding the karma we are experiencing. Why? Because illness can show us our emotional and physical patterns and the nature of personality and lifestyle – all of which is the functioning of karma. Like all true healers and physicians, Tibetan doctors treat karma and its manifestation in the form of emotional and physical illness.

By understanding our karma, we come to know that everything changes, and this shows us how precious our earthly life can be, for our lives are the one dimension of consciousness in which we can under-stand the nature of our karma.

A common misconception is that we are powerless to change the patterns of our lives. In fact, every little thing that helps us to be more conscious enables us slowly to improve the quality of our karmic energy. According to Tibetan teaching, every one of us has the potential to be enlightened and so to live a karma-free life. We may not get there this lifetime but all of us can set about the process of creating good karma now. When you begin to accept the concept of karma, the first stirrings of awareness – however it appears to you – are delightful, thrilling, even mind-blowing. When you treat every person and every event in your life as a gift to help you on your spiritual journey, the way you perceive your life changes.

You begin to see the purpose. You feel connected.

THE ATTITUDE OF ILLNESS

Illness arises from an attitude deep within us, conditioning how we react to all kinds of suffering. This attitude comes from how we see ourselves in this world and the type of lessons that we have to learn. We often say how unfair it is when someone sweet and kind gets a fatal disease, or when young children get ill. How can such innocent beings be allowed to suffer in such a way?

The reason why we become ill is that our underlying attitude is dealing with the lessons we need to learn as a result of past actions and thoughts. Physical pain or mental anguish are the same, and create karma. Sometimes the problem is exacerbated by the body unsuccessfully trying to resolve the illness, then mind and personality can go to war with body and behaviour.

Everyone on this planet is working out some karmic process of cause and effect. What we call illness is the result of a karmic attitude taking control of the body or the mind. Even great spiritual leaders are in the thrall of very subtle attitudes which cause them sickness or other forms of suffering. Other people's interaction can affect your karma, and yours can affect theirs. For example, His Holiness the Dalai Lama and all the great Buddhist and Bön teachers have suffered terribly due to the invasion of Tibet by the Chinese. According to many masters in different Tibetan traditions, this was prophesied many centuries ago and was caused by profound karmic interactions between China and Tibet.

Once these attitudes are in full swing, it can be difficult to change our mental process, particularly if the illness is serious and our bodies are deeply weak and unable to function. When the vital dynamics of the physical body lose strength, the mind may separate from the body. That is when these attitudes have, according to Tibetan medicine, poisoned the vitality of the body-mind connection. The body grieves at the loss of the mind, and the mind panics with no body to carry its messages into the material world. The result is confusion. The vicious cycle continues as this confusion traps the illness, compressing it into sensations of unhappiness and fatigue, and preventing any transformation into positive energy and recovery.

This problem arises when people cannot discern that the world is made up of interconnecting energies: mental, physical and spiritual. These are the underlying and contributing energies known as the three humours, Wind, Bile and Phlegm, which we will explore in other chapters throughout the book. For now it is enough to say that the more separate a person's view of the world, the more strongly the karmic influence is expressed in illness.

Illness is here to help us stay connected to the ordinary events of life, and to remind us of our spiritual, emotional and physical needs. We become ill because we forget our place in the natural cycle. The further we are removed from the concept of illness, the more likely we are to become ill. But, if we grow in self-knowledge and take responsibility for our thoughts and actions, we will slowly become aware of *why* we suffer and become ill.

DEATH, REBIRTH AND REINCARNATION

Karma is being created and worked out from moment to moment, day to day and life to life. When people die they do not disappear, they change form. They then go through a rebirth, which is comparatively better or worse than the life they just left.

First of all, let us clear up the confusion between reincarnation and rebirth. Many people today talk about how problems, events, illness or success come to them because of experiences from past lives. They talk about reincarnation and rebirth as if they are the same. But there is a big difference. When we die, the majority of us go through the process of dying, with all the worries and confusions we carried in life. Because this stops us being clear-minded in the death state, our next life happens without us directly choosing it. And the next, and the next, and so on. This is rebirth. We are endlessly blown around existence by our own desires and karma.

Rare individuals, however, are able to choose the time, place, duration and nature of their lives. That is reincarnation – the process of highly developed consciousness choosing where it goes. Such people could also, if they decided, choose not to be born again. For most of us, the most important life is the one we lead now – the years we have lived since we were born this time. Studying the nature of this present life gives us insight about how to live in the future.

Karma and the birth process

So how do we become reborn? Well, it's a mixture of luck, timing, mental attitude and karma. There is no shortage of wombs, but there is a shortage of good lives into which we can be born. Imagine you are bouncing around in the *bardo*, the state that we enter into between death, birth and life as a human being. Your consciousness craves a physical outlet and, driven by karmic energy, you are drawn closer to your next parents as they make love. With a wallop and a bang, your sex is decided. Powerful emotions drive you to be a boy attracted to your mother, or a girl drawn to the father. You conceive a forceful dislike for the other parent at the moment of conception. Subtle karmic forces are set up for the rest of your life. Because of this, it can be easy for an individual to act out behaviour that was only relevant to conception and time spent in the womb.

PREGNANCY

Towards the end of pregnancy, your mother's womb feels like a solitary confinement cell in the worst prison imaginable. The baby form you inhabit experiences depression, anger, lust and greed, as well as feeling toxic and polluted because the womb is full of poisons. The actual moment of birth is no bed of roses because the birth process is similar to being beaten, or feeling that you are being burnt alive.

The nature and length of the birth process is conditioned by your incoming karma, and how it interacts with the karma of your parents. Sometimes this is beneficial in that it creates good family relationships; other times it will create clumsy family relationships. All of this creates long-term psychological conditioning of your emerging personality.

Hard times

Karmic events in our lives normally go in patterns of threes or fours, with each situation rapidly following the last. So if you are experiencing a succession of problems of such intensity and significance that they cause you anxiety or despair, or reduce you to a state of feeling that you have no control over life, the underlying cause is karma working itself out. It may also be that these are life-changing events from which you can learn so that your life will get better — though maybe not immediately. Remember that karma is not a force against us; we have created it through our own thoughts and actions, informed by what we believed to be true at the time.

CREATING GOOD KARMA

Becoming aware of karmic processes, and deciding to change our karma for the better, is a profound shift that involves no action — merely a different perception that leads you gently into different ways of being and thinking and doing. As we understand these principles of karma, we reveal to ourselves the underlying flow of compassion, which is the bedrock of happiness and contentment. But as we uncover this compassion — exposing it in public — our everyday minds often go into a state of shock or even rebellion.

This happens because the more underlying self-knowledge we allow ourselves to see, the more the mundane habits of our lives become unglued. Our everyday minds are addicted to the comfort of their familiar routines, so, when they sense a threat, they throw up all sorts of land mines and smoke screens to prevent us delving further.

If we forge on, we see that although many of our routines are valuable and sensible, they can restrict our lives and put brakes on our spiritual journey. We can, however, transform the energy we put into everyday activities in simple ways. However humble and commonplace they are, each becomes a window through which we can see the divine. Like a baby chick cracking open the egg, that is the awakening of our own inner enlightenment.

<~>

An American patient of mine came to me deeply unhappy. Financially he was well off, but mentally he had entered into a cold and isolated state. He told me that he was a drug dealer. I suggested that this is a line of work which causes suffering to others and to himself.

After we had discussed it, he decided to return all his drug-dealing money to the communities that he had affected. In a Bön ritual of purification, he burnt all the rest of his money, dollar by dollar; as he did so, he went through extreme psychic and physical pain. This process allowed him to start to burn off his self-made pollution.

He later turned himself in to the police and served time in prison. One of the drug squad that he confessed to is now a close friend. On his release he started a successful new business, which funds a nation-wide drug charity programme that he set up.

This man found a spiritual path and also a loving wife. He turned his karma around by taking responsibility for his actions.

GENEROSITY HEALS ALL THINGS

Generosity is the first step on the path to improving your karma. This combination of emotional and intellectual energy is the single force that will help to burn away negative karmic patterns that may stop us from having the life we want. Generosity heals all things and is part of the natural goodness that exists within us all.

Generosity is not just giving things to other people in order that they will benefit. Primarily, it is giving with compassion and humour so that as well as benefiting the recipient, the energy of your generosity empowers them. They feel good in receiving what you offer. This attracts good fortune to them and thus radiates generosity into the world. Like the common cold, generosity can be easily caught and spread. It is a naturally spontaneous action, but it can also be planned and directed so that it becomes a skill that expresses our natural goodness.

Religion and philosophy often cause a greater lack of generosity than any other human activity. They are nothing more than buckets in which to carry refreshments for our souls to snack on. If you truly wish to experience an energy that can transform suffering and heal deep-seated karmic patterns for yourself and others, you must know that, within all life, there exists only one true teaching: love and kindness. There is nothing else.

Generosity and equality

The world may talk about equality but, in fact, all living creatures are born unequal because the machinery of power uses inequality as its fuel. Some people are more unequal than others. Equality will only come about as the karmic patterns in this planet lose their grip and transmute into new ways of interaction. Generosity of spirit, mind and action is the first step in enabling all living creatures to become equal because implicit within true generosity is compassion, and that is inescapably linked to the necessity of acting with responsibility to all things. Every little kindness that you do is a powerful step towards the gradual equality of all life on earth.

How to develop generous energy

Be generous in the way your heart tells you to be. Never be generous because you think you should. This is an unskilful mental action that will create clumsy events in the world around you and complicate your karmic patterns. Do not expect generosity to be returned. If you do, it becomes a business transaction, and you start to develop the habit of weighing up value and worth. This diminishes your emotions, life force and mind, and creates further confusing karmic situations.

RESULTS OF LIVING GENEROUSLY

When you are truly generous, the material energies of karma often create a process whereby life offers up a 'thank-you' in the form of material benefit. But do not go looking for it, or life may slap you in the face. Generosity not only destroys negativities to do with work and financial success, but also helps to liberate you from inner fears and emotional conflicts of any type. Generosity creates thankfulness, so you start to live your life as a blessing. Being thankful for what you have is an act of generosity towards yourself.

This gratitude teaches you to become less attached to what you have and who you are. Paradoxically, this means that you value your material world more because you are creating more emotional space which will be filled by positive energy. You are also free to love more widely and sincerely because you will be less attached to creating situations in which you hope to receive love from particular people.

As we work through our karma, we begin to understand that such love and kindness are simple and pure. It is often difficult to comprehend this. Karma can twist itself around love and kindness like a pretty scented weed, shooting off rampageously in many directions. There are many good things about this weed; not least, that it heals us from doubt and fear. But eventually we must let it die and be reborn as a simple, unshowy healing herb.

By understanding the shifting patterns of karma in this way – from weed to herb – we can help to heal ourselves and find happiness, which is part of the natural cycle of our consciousness. And being happy helps us to recognise that life is essentially a spiritual experience.

A SINGLE THOUGHT CAN CHANGE YOUR LIFE FOREVER

Thinking is a skill that leads to self-knowledge. Self-knowledge is wisdom that is available to each and every one of us. Wisdom activates your consciousness. So thinking well is good medicine. Most of the time, however, we don't think with the intention of creating an event or situation that can enhance our life: we think only in reaction to what has happened to us. One powerful way to create positive thoughts that support you to have a happy life is improving the way in which you think, speak and act.

For example, if you work for many years, months or even days in a job you really hate, it will cause you to create negative behaviour due to the negative emotions and thought patterns that build up within you. This creates a psychic pressure that hurts your emotional stability and diminishes your sense of well-being.

<~>

Harvey had worked for many years as a stockbroker. Since childhood he had experienced a great sense of loneliness. He thought that by making money he would feel safe and comfortable, and defend himself against loneliness.

After decades of incredible success, his work environment became intolerable. Harvey then did something that all his colleagues dreamed of, but did not have the courage to do. He set up his own company. The economy was unhealthy and everyone said he would fail. In fact, he succeeded beyond his wildest dreams. But within a short space of time Harvey began to feel as he had before: unhappy, unfulfilled and under pressure.

One day he woke up realising that all of his working life had been a nightmare. He really hated his job and working for himself intensified this experience. He lost interest. Slowly, other colleagues in his own company conspired to get rid of him.

When they succeeded in removing Harvey from his own company, he realised deep inside that he just didn't care. He started growing and selling organic apples and flowers. He made his own honey and discovered his inner happiness. He realised how the single thought of making money had caused him anxiety throughout his entire life. When he gave up this thought, he became happy.

This is just one example of the way in which millions of people all over the world are creating negative or obstructional karma when, in fact, they don't need to suffer like this. Even when financial pressure is the root cause of the situation, we can look within ourselves to find answers to change the circumstances.

<~>

How to think better

Thoughts are the starting point for both words and actions. Our world is ruled by the energy of thought, but it is not until we learn to think in a creative and responsible way that we can understand this truth. Remember that, according to Tibetan teaching, a thought – skilful or unskilful – is a fully developed situation that has yet to happen. It is in this situation of potentiality that the karmic process is ready to move from a dormant state into an active force, bringing what we regard as good or bad situations.

Some of these situations are dramatic highs and lows, but for most of the time our karma simply brings a continual flow of experiences, routines and habits. Although they may appear to be mundane, they are of great spiritual importance. To understand our karmic influences, both on ourselves and upon other people, we need to know more about the energy of thought, both in terms of our own thinking and that of other people. Unskilful thoughts attract negative energy, which in turn creates unskilful events, actions and outcomes. Clear and skilful thinking, however, brings harmony, contentment and peace.

First you need to understand the kind of thinking patterns you have formed in the past, and then to analyse the results of thinking in that way. There are five types of unskilful thinking patterns that can simultaneously chatter in our minds. These can be seen in every culture across the ages. If you consider that they are the foundations and habits of the way most people conduct their lives, it's easy to see why our society is ill. Unskilful thinking pollutes the mind, which in turn pollutes the world. All of these thinking patterns can create good or bad results; the key is to learn what they have to teach you.

UNSKILFUL THINKING PATTERNS

1. Thinking patterns that make you unrealistically optimistic.

Optimism is a natural impulse in thinking. Over-optimism is an energy that is not refined and balanced. Overly optimistic people are more prone to creating fantasies that they know will not come true, than a realistic blueprint from which to work. Although they genuinely like others, people who think like this often feel essentially lonely. The more you fall into thinking patterns that make you overly optimistic, the more disconnected you become from your emotions. If it is not harmonised, this impulse can cause emotional exhaustion. From a Tibetan medical view, it can also lead to a growing state of inner panic and anxiety that can contribute to the thinker becoming susceptible to cancers of the throat, lungs or thyroid. Lower-back conditions, migraine and phobic cycles also come from this state.

A good thinker is an architect of consciousness. Skilful thinking is the process of assembling invisible energy and constructing an edifice that makes ideas or events real. If we can become skilful thinkers, there will be both social, cultural and global change of huge importance. Individuals will start to become more responsible for their actions. We will understand the need for mutual co-operation. We will feel the impact of thought as it is thought, and the world will become linked by an empathic connection which will help to determine our societies at large, bringing greater social integration. We will be at the beginning of understanding each other.

2. Thinking patterns that lead you to be fearful, gloomy and depressed:

Virtually all of us feel afraid and low at some point in our lives. However, when someone's thinking pattern starts to involve these mental states on a regular or daily basis, Tibetan medicine says that the mind is reacting to karmic forces created because the individual has been overwhelmed by the world around them.

Normally people who experience these states live in fear of communicating with other people. The concept of shyness covers this experience to a degree, but at the heart of this fear of communicating is really a deep sense of isolation and abandonment. If this state is not healed, the person may become susceptible to addictive behaviours, mental illness, skin conditions and problems with the central nervous system in later life.

3. Thinking patterns in which you are focused solely on material outcomes such as money, career and relationships

Focusing your attention completely on having possessions, and control of people, resources and events, money and worldly goods, eventually becomes the equivalent of committing a slow suicide. People who do this have forgotten how to live. They have become divorced from life. Sadly, there are millions living like this globally, creating social unrest and a slow rotting of social integrity, which exerts an unseen pressure on others to conform.

You may say that it's understandable, even admirable, for a poor person to think obsessively about money and work. But it actually decreases their opportunities for advancement because their obsessive thinking starts to build up within them, creating mental piles of rubbish. The more narrowly we focus, the more opportunities we lose for change. We risk becoming caught up in acting out the obsession and not the goal.

People who focus on relationships do so because they hope that the person or people on whom they are focusing will enable them to gain control of their own situation. Equally, people who make themselves the centre of attention are using others as buffers to defend them against the imagined harshness of their lives.

If a wealthy person has tunnel vision about work and money, it stems from a lack of faith in their achievements: they feel that fundamentally they have no value. I know a billionaire who is trapped by the world he has made. He has no faith in what he has achieved, yet he feels he must organise everything so that it can continue. He sleeps little, dresses humbly and drives a small car, not because he wishes to be anonymous, but because he has no sense of value about his wealth or achievements. He is scared of people and he is starting to find out why.

Sometimes people like that focus exclusively on intense relationships with one special person or group of people. This is because they want to like and approve of themselves. The people they are looking at are mirrors which reflect the image that the individual wants to see and believe in.

These types of people are susceptible to arthritis, rheumatism, gout, Parkinson's disease, Steele's syndrome, and a wide range of inflammatory and nervous system diseases. Cancers of the gall bladder, liver and bowel are also common.

4. Thinking patterns where you obsess about physical and sexual activities

When a person dwells only on these matters, it is because they are emotionally and spiritually stuck. It is not because they seek emotional intimacy that they think like this. They do so because they unconsciously feel that they have lost the connection to the spiritual energies of their personality and to the world around them. So they focus upon physical or sexual activities to discover vitality and energy, and to feel connected and alive.

Illness of the musculo-skeletal system is common to these types of thinkers, as are sudden bouts of depression. Most experience great loneliness in later life.

5. Thinking patterns that make you focused on spiritual, artistic or religious activities, while denying the material world, your own culture and its influence upon you.

This type of thinking pattern takes place because the person is consumed with the search for truth and meaning, but is pursuing it in an unskilful and unproductive manner. Spiritual transformation, artistic endeavour or religious vocation of any lasting value comes through some form of interaction with your own culture, material realities and art. These are the catalysts and mediums through which constructive and liberating thinking patterns take place in this life.

This type of thinker is susceptible to addictions of any type, mental illness, all forms of cancer, dental illnesses, and conditions affecting the reproductive organs, the eyes and sight. They also tend to dislike humanity, disregard authority and be culturally intolerant.

The more you know about these negative thinking patterns, the more you will be able to engage in constructive thinking. Simply being aware of them allows you to start clearing your mind of these untamed thoughts and the emotional pain they create. You can do this by looking deeply within yourself for a few minutes every day and reflecting on whether any or all are moving within you. Surprisingly quickly, you will gain insight into how such thought processes affect you personally, and also how you affect other people and the world around you. This in turn reduces the general karmic fall-out in your life.

As your mental and spiritual energies become stronger, the general level of your thinking becomes more powerful, as does the quality of your emotional experiences. The process of weaving your own karma will also become profound, effortlessly. You will find yourself imbued with a deeper sense of responsibility for the way you think and behave, to yourself and to all living creatures. If you decide to accept this responsibility, you will begin to understand that all living things seek to communicate.

What they want to communicate is wisdom, happiness and the unconditional compassion that flows through us all and that is our foundation as living creatures.

CHAPTER FOUR
Awaken the Wisdom Within

*E*ach of us has an infinite capacity for wisdom if we choose to connect with it. Wisdom is not a beginning or an end in itself, it is the process by which we can transform our physical and emotional worlds. It changes and adapts itself to the forces and circumstances around it. The goal is to discover and liberate our consciousness so that each of us can discover the divine in everything and, through that, joy and the immeasurable possibilities of life.

Wisdom comes in many forms, but its underlying essence is the force, or energy, that holds the material and the natural worlds together. It is in every living thing on this planet, regardless of appearances. It is the song of nature; it has rhythms, pulses and beat. Listening to the rhythms of wisdom enables you to become connected to the life force of the planet. Connecting with wisdom enables you to use the energy of thoughts and actions skilfully.

Many people are confused about the nature of wisdom because they see it as influence over other people. That is confusing wisdom with its effect. According to the ancient Tibetans, true wisdom is wisdom over oneself. No one can rob you of your potential for wisdom. You don't need to wear it like a badge; it has no need to show itself unless it is needed.

There is no such thing as perfect wisdom or perfect knowledge about wisdom. It is entwined in the essence of each human being, so it is just as variable as we are. It does not need to be forced, merely understood. Then it naturally enables you.

Connecting with wisdom comes through winning the battle of the heart. This is the war between emotion and intellect, right and wrong, good and bad. It is won when you know the nature of your personality. True wisdom manifests itself in relationships with other people, and one of its great qualities is that it enables you to behave with compassion, humility and good humour in all things.

The starting place is simple, although the path may be testing. You need to be prepared to be full of love. This means learning to accept all the hardship and obstructions in your life so that you can begin to strip away the emotional junk that we all carry.

When consciousness is stuck in matter, as it is in this incarnation, we can become seduced into believing that the material things that enthral our senses are valid and necessary. Inner wisdom helps us to cast out addictions to glamour, gurus and everything that take us away from who we really are and can be.

Exercising wisdom is a natural process that is constantly available to those who are prepared to look beyond the appearances of the everyday world. People are afraid of looking for wisdom because they are frightened of looking too closely at themselves. But if you are able to live with yourself in this way – opening the windows of your perception to look beyond the routine, superficial and mundane – life responds to you with open arms and an open heart.

We can experience this quite simply by not entering into a state of judgement about people, situations and events. Just accept them as they are, without criticism or comment. Instead of being judgmental, be discerning. Being judgmental is unskilful emotional behaviour because you colour a person, situation or event with your own prejudice. Being discerning means trying to be open at all times, to allow knowledge to come to you naturally. Be, think, do what feels right. Feel the energy in this approach. All things will reveal themselves to you if your heart is open.

The world seeks to give all that they want to those who know how to ask. For those who are one with their wisdom, the skill of asking and the gift of receiving come naturally. Tasting the sweetness of your inner wisdom releases many answers to the questions that you have about life, and the issues that are important to you. Although, paradoxically, you may often not really know the question until you have received the answer. Then you suddenly realise that it was something that had been bothering you for ages.

The issues can be about anything or anyone — trusting that an important favour had been carried out by a friend, for instance, or that a job you had paid for was completed. Nagging doubts about anything — from the unimportant to the crucial in the past, present or future — are resolved through information and circumstances coming together.

Being connected to wisdom does not mean that your life will be free of problems or difficulties. But you will know how to solve, transform and release them so that they will not repeat themselves again. There are many benefits. Being connected to this wisdom in our daily lives acts as a stabiliser and a healing force, and will often show us the direction we should take in life. Also, acting wisely in your everyday life energises the people around you.

As you connect with your wisdom, you will discover the meaning of an ancient Tibetan principle: 'All community comes from the community of one.' This means that once you are united with your inner wisdom, there are no divisions or conflicts in your life. All material aspects of mind — intellect, emotions and everyday living — flow from your consciousness in one coherent stream.

True wisdom sustains everything.

THE STARTING POINT

It is the knowledge that our life has meaning that enables us to experience both wisdom and pleasure. It is meaning that gives wisdom its value and ultimate use. If there were no point to our lives, why would we want or need wisdom?

Through the years there are signposts that offer us opportunities to understand what meaning our life has. We can learn to recognise the special omens that will lead us to turning points.

We must start with an experience to which all human beings are

attracted: beauty. Beauty is a doorway to wisdom and can be an expression of it. The ancient Tibetans believed that beauty can be a way to
understand the nature of the material world because as material beauty
fades, spiritual beauty grows. Connecting with our own inner beauty
allows us to discover that we are sacred. This is what beauty is for, a
display of sacredness in the material world.

By knowing the nature of inner and outer beauty, you can activate
it within you and in your life.

HOW TO RELEASE IMMENSE WISDOM: THE EIGHT MATERIAL ACTIVITIES

People in ancient Tibet were no different from people in today's world:
they too had troubles, doubts and fears. But, nowadays, because of the
pressures of modern living – commuting, work stress, crime, unemploy-
ment and all the other problems we live with daily – we cannot see
how to make our problems better. The key is to know the energy at
the core of our problems.

This is revealed by examining what the Tibetan Bön and Buddhist
traditions call the 'eight material activities'. These describe the nature
of our feelings. They are the mental building blocks that fuel all human
endeavour and influence the way we respond to the events and people
in our lives. They are: loss, shame, guilt and suffering; and achievement, fame, approval and happiness.

Whether seemingly negative (the first four) or positive (the second
group) the material activities have immense power over our lives. We
absorb these characteristics from childhood and then start to use them
to define our everyday realities. They create confusion in our minds,
handcuffing us to a desperate search for what we believe is happiness,
and an equally intense desire to avoid unhappiness. You have only to

look at your life and those of other people to see how we are all affected.

The results of being handcuffed to these feelings are unpredictable and often uncontrollable. Wisdom comes when we can see that the eight material activities are born from anger, lust and greed. They urge people to create and to destroy. We may long for, say, approval but in chasing it, we damage others and expose ourselves to shame. We take an important job, not because we really want to do it, but for the status and money it brings. We have a relationship with someone, not because we truly love and empathise with them, but because we bask in the security of their approval.

The wise action is to cut the cords of attachment to all the material activities, the positive as well as the negative, so that our lives are not defined by them. This makes us truly free.

To do this we must learn to accept all the aspects of our personality – the light and the dark – without judgement, and to understand that both happiness and unhappiness are good. Then we can receive and give thanks for the good times and for the bad.

True wisdom comes from the mind and creates its own freedom. Understanding the energy wielded by these material activities helps to take away their influence over you. You become able to use your energy, thoughts and actions skilfully and appropriately. You surrender your fears and become more compassionate and patient. You will find that your life naturally starts to improve and good fortune to flow in.

The ancient Tibetans often described the way in which our emotions influence us as a turbulent mountain river. This is a traditional Bön story, which illustrates the different ways in which three people are conditioned by the eight material activities.

<~>

A man stood on the edge of a river. Although it was narrow, the current was strong. The angry water seemed an image of his mind, throbbing and tossing with the eight material activities. He decided to let them flow out of his mind into the water. His mind became calm and his heart content.

Suddenly he heard a shout for help and in the white foam of the waves he saw a man from his village. He hated this man because he had had sex with his wife, stolen his livestock and then beaten him at wrestling. Then another cry for help came to his ears. In the water he saw a very holy saint whom he respected greatly. He had helped him in times of trouble and had eased his mind.

Both men were being dragged to the edge of a dangerous waterfall. He knew they would be drowned. With great effort he hurled his hunting rope to the other side. The noose tightened fast around a rock and he tied the other end to a tree.

Both men caught on to the rope and pulled themselves to safety. But once on the riverbank they began to fight. The holy man started screaming, 'I tried to stop you jumping in and you pulled me in with you. Now look at me! I'm soaking wet.'

The other man just laughed hysterically and punched the holy man on the nose. 'You do-gooders are all the same,' he said. 'I never asked you to help me.'

At this, our brave hero became upset and confused, and his body tensed up. Then he suddenly realised that *these men were not real but personifications of the eight material activities.*

With a yell he pushed them back into the river and they plunged screaming over the waterfall down into the seething water. He sat on the riverbank exhausted, the screaming still echoing in the rocky gorge around him.

But doubt sneaked into his mind like a thief. He started panicking about pushing the two men back into the waterfall. What if he was wrong . . . ?

<~>

This story illustrates the subtle pervasiveness of the eight material activities. Here is a man wanting to be at peace by ridding himself of the activities. As he lets them flow from his mind, he experiences the achievement of peace and contentment. But when he sees his enemy drowning, he feels shame, loss, guilt, suffering and also happiness. Then he notices the holy man and experiences happiness and the lure of fame. When his enemy and the holy man start fighting, he goes through shame, loss, guilt and suffering. Then he experiences the relief of recognising that they must be an illusion created by the eight material activities. Peace again. He can push both men back into the river because they are not real. Then his everyday mind comes up with a new problem. Just suppose he was wrong?

<~>

How to Connect with Inner Wisdom by Living in the Space Between Moments

Memories glue our lives together. Memories are moments. Moments are frozen experiences, squeezed out of the eight material activities. Life is a series of these moments which turn into the blur we call reality.

Many of us believe that we should try to live in the present moment, but this is unwise for two reasons. Our brains cannot experience reality directly because everything has to be received and interpreted through our senses. So we live in the past, always a few seconds behind. We can't experience the moment directly; it has passed before we can even comprehend it.

Furthermore, moments are entire worlds of experience, immensely huge and complex. To live in the moment with our everyday mind would be almost impossible. It would risk making us nearly as frantic and busy, exhausted and unconnected to the world around us as living in the past and the future do.

The place to live is not in the moment, but in the space between moments – a space that holds a continual flow of wisdom and consciousness. By connecting to the space between the moments of your life you start to experience what is, not what was.

Wisdom is everywhere, waiting to be received and used. But we only begin to understand wisdom when we are at our most humble, and we can only go beyond the moment into the space between when we truly understand that the only thing separating the everyday world and the world of wisdom is a transparent curtain.

Think of a time in your own life when you had nowhere and no one to turn to outside yourself. In that state of not being able to cope, there is an inner dialogue taking place between your frightened everyday mind – which is made up of the eight material activities – and your inner wisdom, which consists of nothing but itself.

If, in those situations, you can enter the space between moments and rest in your wisdom, you will find that it will comfort your everyday mind, allay its fears and allow it to start afresh. You are all the wisdom you need.

How to enter the space between moments: a meditation

Make yourself comfortable, sitting, lying down or in a favourite meditation position. Close your eyes and look within yourself as far as you can see. You will sense an inner horizon. When you reach it, look beyond. When you can see no more, rest within yourself. This looking inwards sometimes gives the sensation of travelling within yourself.

In this place of rest, listen to your inner world. Slowly you will hear the rumbling of your everyday mind: it may sound like a train, a storm or a large crowd of people talking at once. Listen again and under that you will hear a slow and exquisite sound, like a soloist singing a beautiful song, a choir, the playing of a cello or a distant wind. That is your inner wisdom.

Don't feel you have to do anything with this wisdom when you find it. Just allow it to percolate naturally into your life. Be with it. You will find that simply knowing it's there – remembering the way it appeared to you, sensing its nature – will take you naturally into the space between moments and allow this experience to become second nature in your daily life.

You can do this meditation once a day for as long or short a time as you wish. Do not force or regiment it; you will find a natural cycle develops and this will guide you.

Inner wisdom can change the outer world. Experiencing the space between moments may take just a second and permeate your entire life, creating opportunities for dynamic change and healing. The sacred stillness that stays in our everyday mind is the fountainhead of the constant wisdom that flows through our life and the natural world. The way your mind works, how you view the world, and your feelings about life can all be refreshed and restored.

Using the eight material activities to diagnose the cause of your inner troubles

Understanding the material activities and how they affect you can help you to create a balanced life. The stories below tell of two people who experienced every one of them and of how their lives suffered in consequence.

By using the meditation technique above to tune in to the dialogue between their inner wisdom and their everyday mind, they were able to gain insight into how and why they had suffered. They understood how they created their problems, reacted to them and then played them out.

This understanding empowered them to live a more skilful life and to create real happiness. Their stories highlight the way in which people can turn things around, if they really want to.

<~>

Like most of us, Laurent, a singer, and Bruce, a doctor, had allowed the eight material activities to become the foundation of their existence. From their perspective at the time, they believed they had experienced them positively. In their different ways, both had star-spangled careers that brought them fame, status and approval. Neither experienced shame, loss or guilt in their lives. Other people saw them as members of the 'great and good' club. But then it all went wrong.

At 55, Laurent was at the peak of her career as a country and western singer in North America. She seemed to have it all: constant success, huge amounts of money and an adoring husband and family. She was loved and idolised across the world.

But inside, Laurent felt empty and shoddy, as if she was made of mud and straw. On tour, audiences noticed that she had lost her spark. Slowly her career dried up and she found herself at home in her mansion with nothing to do and nowhere to go.

Then one of Laurent's two daughters died in a plane crash. Later, the other was seriously injured in a car accident. Laurent started to drink too much. Her husband ran away with her best friend, taking a large amount of Laurent's money with them. Laurent's drinking declined into alcoholism.

Completely lost, Laurent came to see me. As she began to recover from the pain of betrayal and of her alcohol addiction, we discussed the eight material activities and how they had been expressed in her life. They gave her an insight into why her life had fallen to pieces.

'My whole life was based on one big false image and I believed it so much that I didn't allow myself to see that, deep inside, I knew the truth. My inner self was yelling at me to wake up but I couldn't hear – didn't want to hear – until it all came crashing down.'

Laurent knew each of the material activities had contributed to her obsessive drive for money and fame from an early age. Now she understood that they were covering up a spiritual need that had never been fulfilled. She realised that her old life had weak foundations and that her everyday mind functioned only by knee-jerk reactions — conditioned by the material activities — to every event in her life. As her true personality eroded so her life fell to pieces, because the blueprint to which she was working was flawed.

Today, Laurent has a new life with a different focus — her own happiness. Day by day, she is recovering from her alcoholism. No longer does she use her fame to gloss over her problems. She does the occasional concert, singing for joy rather than for money and status, and her musical career has recently taken off again. She hasn't met a new love, but she isn't worried. She feels connected to herself and to the world. She is content.

<~>

Bruce, a celebrated trauma specialist in the Accident and Emergency department of a big hospital in the deep south of America, saved lives daily. Quiet-mannered and softly spoken, everyone looked up to him as a perfectionist who could always be relied on. Behind the calm facade, however, was a different story.

Bruce himself was traumatised by the suffering of his patients — victims of violent crime or appalling accidents — and by the fear of failing in front of his colleagues. Driven by his own demons, he became more and more successful. He believed his work made him happy until something within him began to fail. He made a wrong diagnosis, his patient died and a court case followed where he was publicly shamed.

The man who could do no wrong was now reviled

by his community. There was no one to fight his corner, none of the approval on which he had depended for years. He broke down.

When Bruce came to see me, he told me that he had started to lose his spirit long before making the misdiagnosis. He was on burn-out. Like Laurent, he was falling to pieces. His breakdown was the end of a long process.

As Bruce learned the meditation practice above, he started to realise how all the eight material activities had conditioned his life. He felt he had become a walking, talking machine fuelled by material aspirations — money, house, car, fame, sex — which were far from the reasons he originally went into medicine. He had forgotten his desire to make sick people healthy and the world a better place.

As we talked, he remembered an inner conviction that he'd had from early on — that there is something inside human beings that influences our lives and our state of health. Something that makes us sick or well. Curiously, it was something that he had buried during his career in medicine.

This realisation was the beginning of his exploration into the relationship between his everyday mind and his inner wisdom. Along the way he found that despite the shame and guilt of his patient's death, he was a worthwhile person.

Today, Bruce is working again as a physician, but this time in a desert community, far from the bright lights and big city environment he craved before. Rather than patching up broken bodies, he heals emotional and

physical ills. He uses the eight material activities as
one of his diagnostic tools, working with his patients
to uncover their underlying problems.

Bruce says he feels happier now. He knows who
he is and he wants to help other people to do the same.

<~>

Everyone has the power to awaken the wisdom within. We only have to try. All we have to lose is our unhappiness. Look inside. Listen to the dialogue between the everyday mind and the inner wisdom. They seek to communicate so that you may become whole, happy and empowered.

STARTING OVER: BREATHING A NEW PERSONA

The simplest and most basic way you can start your new life is through breathing. We are what we breathe and we are because we breathe. It is the spirit of life.

According to Tibetan wisdom, the universe is a living, breathing organism. Breath is the underlying psychic make up of the material universe, connecting everything in the cosmos. So every breath we inhale and exhale links us to the in and out of the universe.

This connection through the nature of the breath is more than just physical; it is essential in creating our humanity and consciousness. Breathing gives us the ability to love and the breathing patterns that we develop also dictate our attitudes towards money, material achieve-ment and our attitudes towards success and failure.

Tibetan wisdom states that, although we breathe automatically, breathing is not an unconscious action. The problem is that through our unthinking, clumsy attitude, we have come to treat it as if it was. By learning to master the huge resource that exists within our breathing, each of us can reveal our potential. Deep in the process of respiration is practical wisdom which can be released to our conscious mind

There are nine dimensions of breathing; each of which can empower an aspect of our personality. Let us now explore each of these and how they build the energetic architecture that creates the foundations of everyone's persona. You will find a simple meditation with each, which will help you to absorb them into your life. With this, you can use your breathing – your respiration – to inspire your life.

Choose calm and peaceful environments when you meditate: uncross your arms and legs, close your eyes and relax. But don't worry if the only place you can find is at your desk or on a bus – just do the best you can. Breathe gently and rhythmically. In these meditations you will focus mainly on a negative situation: be sure not to judge yourself harshly. Just be loving to yourself and to the problem.

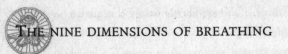

THE NINE DIMENSIONS OF BREATHING

1. PERSONALITY AND EMOTION

This first stage influences the way in which we interact with the world around us, and the intensity of our emotions. It is in this stage that all our self-knowledge exists, waiting to be activated. Our first breath at birth sets the emotional nature of our personality for the rest of our lives – unless and until we choose to change it. Breathing sets up the personality, so meditating on this first cycle can help you to reinvent your life.

Meditation

Reflect on whatever you are unhappy with in your personality and your emotions. Try and define what doesn't feel right and look at it without judging yourself. For instance, if you feel you have a problem with anger, or gossiping, or being negative, start off by saying to yourself: 'I am aware that I get angry/gossipy/negative and of the effect that has on me and on other people.'

Repeat this several times. Take a slow breath in, hold it for a few seconds, then breathe out slowly. This will help to purify and transform your anger, or other negative characteristics.

You can do this simple meditation for any conflict you feel within you, or for any personality trait that you want to transform. Do it for ten minutes, twice a day, for 27 days.

2. INTELLECT

As the first stage creates our emotional reality, so the second creates our intellectual ability. The intensity, quality and nature of our intellect is set up by this breathing cycle. This breathing pattern affects us all the time, as our intellectual abilities are constantly changing.

Your emotional energy dominates intellect and all the other dimensions. But your intellectual energy cannot change your emotions.

Meditation

If you find it hard to think clearly or to concentrate on an intellectual or academic discipline of any sort, you can stimulate the second dimension of your breath by focusing on a conflict or subject that is causing you a problem. Breathe in and out, focusing on the issue, then imagine that your intellect is a single flame flowing down into the power centre in your navel. Breathe in the flame, hold it for a moment, then breathe it out, directing the fiery energy to your mind. This will purge your intellect, burning away the confusion.

3. PHYSICAL HEALTH

This third breathing pattern directly influences your body's state of health. It is the one pattern of which most people are aware. When we become ill, our breathing will always change.

By understanding the nature of breathing in this cycle you can have a direct and powerful influence over your health and physical well-being. Training your breath can show you how your body works and, if it's not working, how to repair it. Good health is actually good insight about your body: discovering this puts you in control.

Meditation

Whether you are currently feeling well or ill, you can practise this meditation to optimise your health. Start by breathing normally. If you are well, focus on your heartbeat and allow your in and out breath to align with it. If you are ill, take long deep breaths, holding your breath between inhaling and exhaling for as long as you comfortably can. Think about the illness and the symptoms. Identify the key words describing your condition and say them to yourself while you breathe out slowly and gently. Do this five times, then again link your breath to your heartbeat.

4. ADAPTABILITY

The fourth stage in the breathing cycle that makes up our personality becomes more dominant whenever mankind as a species is in a period of global change, because it gives us the ability to successfully adapt and change to circumstances and events. It also embodies our potential to create a profound connection with the forces of nature.

According to ancient Tibetan Bön teachings, it was this breathing cycle that dominated every part of human consciousness in the earliest times on earth – an era of vast change. As the species developed and became city-dwellers in Neolithic times, this particular aspect of the breathing cycle diminished. It is only in the last turbulent five hundred years that this aspect of the breathing cycle has returned to common consciousness within the everyday world.

Meditation

This will help if you have trouble in accepting change or find it hard to adapt to changing circumstances. Sit quietly and focus your mind on the situation and circumstances. As you do this, let the essence of the situation come to you: sometimes it seems unlikely, but you will find your instinct is always right. Hold this essential truth as your mantra and chant it aloud as you slowly breathe in and out. Do this once a day, for as long as you are able, for nine consecutive days.

5. WEALTH AND ABUNDANCE

This fifth stage relates to the nature of money, wealth, abundance and resources. By cultivating this aspect of breathing, you start to attract a more harmonious flow of resources to you.

If you are prepared to share what you have, it is your right to have what you need, indeed to have *more* than you need. If at the end of your life you have great wealth and do not share it, you create deep mental obstructions that diminish your happiness before you die.

Good fortune waits within the forces of your unconscious mind so the world of money and abundance responds to this cycle of breathing. You must be ready for it, though, because it can have a more lethal effect upon your mind and emotions than fame. You will only keep it if your heart is also abundant in love and generosity.

Meditation

Sitting quietly with your eyes closed, breathe in and out. Clap your hands together as loud as you can to purify the atmosphere around you. Focus on breathing slowly for a few moments, then in your mind's eye see your inner breathing drawing up wealth and abundance from within you. As you breathe out, direct these out into the world as raw energy. It will automatically come back to you, like a boomerang. To end the meditation, say quietly but firmly out loud, 'I thank the world, I thank all things, I thank my awakening good fortune.' Clap your hands loudly and slowly three time and, if you wish, bow to north, south, east and west and then to the ground beneath your feet.

6. FRIENDSHIP

This cycle relates to our roles as friends and parents. According to Tibetan wisdom, a friend is a person who not only shares the important times in your life, but can also act as a spiritual guide, bringing insight to your needs and dilemmas.

This dimension of breathing reveals how we see ourselves in the world. Our friends are us. We have them because we need them.

When it comes to parents, the process becomes even more acute. Our parents reflect our journey in life, and show us possible karmic experiences that need to be resolved. These karmic experiences are neither good nor bad, just a part of the process that people must go through to gain a more complete self-knowledge. Tuning into this breathing cycle can help us fully comprehend the reasons why we choose the parents and the children that we do.

Meditation

This exercise helps us to connect and care for other people. You can use it to heal problems with friends or family. Sitting silently, close your eyes and direct your attention to the person with whom you are in conflict. As you inhale, imagine that you are breathing them into you. As you exhale, breathe out any negativity. You can do this with a single person, a group, or everyone on the planet. You can simply visualise great crowds as your friends and family, drawing them into your heart and mind with your breath.

7. INTEGRITY AND MORALITY

In the seventh cycle, we discover the process of self-responsibility and the importance of developing integrity and a personal moral code. Morality cannot be taught but it can be experienced by understanding a little of your personality. It is within this cycle that self-empowerment takes place and the search for meaning in life is to be found.

The seventh cycle is profoundly affected by the sixth; the two are often deeply interwined within people's lives. The foundations, structures and habits we have towards personal relationships are played out in this cycle. The sixth can profoundly influence a person's search for love and the seventh is linked to intimate personal relationships.

It is here, also, that the differences between men and women are created on the energetic level. This energy is not just physical and psychological but becomes, for both genders, a special and different experience of the planet.

Meditation

Within you and everyone there exists pure integrity and a deep moral awareness. This exercise will help you to connect with these qualities of your inner nature and experience them in your daily life. Sitting in silence with your eyes closed, focus on your heartbeat. As you breathe in, and out, see your breath creating a light within your physical heart. Pink at first, it glows more powerfully with each breath until it radiates a pure white incandescence that spreads purity and integrity throughout your body and mind. Merge with this white light and the true nature of your inner morality will be clear to you.

8. TRUST

This part of the nine cycles of breathing has a profound association with the experience of trust and safety. Ultimately this has to do with trusting the natural order of life and feeling safe with other people and one's Self in the greater play of life and its circumstances.

The eighth breathing pattern teaches us that all things will ultimately be harmonious. That there is a meaning to the sometimes overwhelming chaos that is casually termed life. Life is not bigger than you or me, but the events of life can seem that way. We have to realise that those events are not life, just incidents that mark the passage of life through your experience of living. You are life, as we all are.

Meditation

In order to trust other people and the world around us we need to connect with the earth. We are children of the earth and dependent on it for all material things; this connection is the bedrock of any form of trust. Find a pebble or handful of soil and sit comfortably, with your eyes closed, holding it. As you breathe in, imagine its energy flowing into you and connecting you directly with the earth. The pebble and the soil are nothing except what they are and that is the nature of pure trust. Do this exercise once a day when you wake up.

9. LIFE DEATH REBIRTH

The last stage in the nine cycles of breathing reveals to us that all things are renewed. It is one of the great beauties of the universe, that all things continue regardless of death or any other kind of ending, whether they take the form of people, rocks, buses or teacups. Death simply means a change of energy and form.

The ninth cycle holds within it the very impulses of life energy. It shadows the other eight, often coming to us in times of introspection or in dreams. It is most active when we are born, again when we have our first sexual experiences, and when we are about to die. It is the essence of the evolution of our species.

Meditation

With your eyes closed, breathe slowly in and out. As you do so, see each in and out breath as a stream of light carrying you deep into the underlying essence of everything, where you can sense the energetic foundations of the universe. As you breathe, let yourself be absorbed into this clear sparkling light. You fuse with the light. You are the light and it is you.

Practise this meditation once a week, building up to one hour, if possible. You will begin to experience the interconnection of all the nine dimensions.

'Your breath is the only thing that you own,' my teacher told me.

Through these meditations you may see that it is the only thing that you need.

CHAPTER FIVE
Emotional Healing

Our emotions are the origins of our physical health. The emotional dynamics within us set up the patterns that are then implemented in our body, where in time they become patterns of well-being or of ill-health. In order to be truly healthy it is vital to understand and balance the emotional dynamics within us.

Few of us can claim, however, that our emotions are in a continuous state of harmony, or that we understand why we feel as we do. The key is our everyday mind. I have talked about this concept in the preceding chapters but it is important to remember that our everyday mind is the survival mechanism we develop to get through the ups and downs of daily life in this incarnation as human beings. It is built up of behaviour, habits, strategies we have learned over the years in response to people, events and situations. It is clever, informed and cunning, but the everyday mind knows very little about itself. In other words, it is not bad but it is ignorant and, although it has enabled us to survive, it does not always act in our best interests.

Behind the everyday mind lies our inner wisdom. This is the foundation of all living creatures. It is pure consciousness.

Our emotions arise from our everyday minds. Emotions are submerged frequencies of energy that undulate in reaction to the way we respond to the world around us and force their way into our waking consciousness. Take a very simple example: it's a sunny day, people smile and say hello, and you feel happy. Emotions are also capable of more sophisticated reactions to others which are sometimes called telepathy: we can, for instance, sometimes sense someone else's unhappiness, even if they are far away and we can't see or hear them. Absent healing is another example. Such apparently paranormal experiences are made possible by the effect of these waves of energy.

Bridging the chasm between our everyday mind and our inner wisdom or consciousness is the linchpin of health, according to Tibetan medical wisdom. Your everyday mind is the catalyst and cause of illness because it creates behaviour that binds you to thought and actions, which in turn cause you pain and illness.

Knowing how to interpret your emotional energy as an indicator of the state of your consciousness is a great asset. Most of the time our minds and bodies are trying to communicate with each other in vain. This blocked communication often creates conflict and disharmony that come out in the shape of anxiety, moodiness, depression, bad temper, shyness, fear and a range of other negative emotions. This then leads to illness of all kinds. You can see the results of frustrated mind-body communication in such common conditions as tension headaches, work-related injuries such as neck and back ache, a nervous tummy, colds and skin conditions. Most Western scientists now agree that emotions play a major part in many serious conditions, including cancer and heart disease.

If we can cultivate deeper connections between the body and the mind, we calm the cycles of confusion and we then have a greater chance of health.

Tibetan emotional healing is a process that uses a combination of your everyday mind and your inner wisdom to understand how you become ill and also how you can recover and stay well. This requires courage, faith in yourself and the awareness that you are the originator of your own states of health and in charge of your own healing process.

If you can see deeply enough within your personality, you will start to understand how any condition, emotional or physical, is caused and how it affects you. This knowledge may not heal you in an obvious way, such as improving physical symptoms, but understanding the nature of any condition leads to opportunities for creating well-being.

Emotional healing enables a person who feels under pressure to become clear minded and relaxed, in order to deal with the require-ments of everyday living. It can also be used to clear the mind so that a person can have direct experience of his or her inner perfection and, further, to gain insight into intellectual or worldly concerns.

The healing is based on understanding seven simple principles, applying these to the key human experiences and then using specific meditations to stimulate the healing process.

THE SEVEN PRINCIPLES

1. Your physical body is still your mind: it is simply the material form of the emotional energy of your mind. Pain, illness and well-being are the products of your everyday mind. Your inner unstained true mind holds all understanding to your ill-health and suffering.

2. Reality is not what it seems: your everyday mind gets its information about the physical world through your senses, but you can't always trust this version. Your senses are taking in information that in seconds becomes the past. So your mind is creating a reality that is seemingly in the moment, but really in the past. Understanding this fundamental fact of life enables you to become aware of how situations are created and develop so that you can intuitively sense the way in which one situation gives rise to another.

3. All of our experiences, past and present, influence the nature and quality of emotional and physical health. They are markers in the way our life energy develops and grows. By understanding and transforming the quality of your life experiences, you reduce the possibility of illness. Left unhealed and misunderstood, they may lead to illness and also affect how well you recover. The way you react to feeling ill or under the weather is also based on all your experiences and how you have responded to illness in the past.

4. Illness or any major crisis in your life is mostly a process of the past catching up with you. This does not includes natural events – such as earthquakes or floods – or accidents, but in many cases, it is the effects of our past thoughts, actions and interactions with other people that influence how and why we become ill. If we can honestly identify the sources of illness or any major crisis, we can start to extinguish the negative forces of the past and transform them into positive experiences.

5. Your physical body is an expression of consciousness and of all time and space in miniature, a microcosm of the macrocosm. You can help your body develop into a higher state of physical intelligence, which enables it to heal itself. This state of body directly and simply expresses the energies of the mind into the world, thereby bringing peace and harmony. This experience unites us with the divine grace of the universe and the god or gods of our understanding, teaching us to honour the lives we have entered and guiding us through difficulties.

In this state, you have a direct understanding of the space between moments and you are able to know reality directly and intimately. Just as your mind can experience this enlightenment so your body can become the physical expression of it. There is no one way in which enlightenment presents itself, because each person's body and mind are unique. Your experience would be different to mine and the next person's but we would all share common qualities.

6. You can heal your mind and body and achieve dynamic well-being by using the pure state of your inner mind. To do this it is necessary to discipline your everyday mind, which will always try to dominate any interchange that involves the conscious connection between it and your body.

You can start to discipline your everyday mind by observing the way you react to problems:

- Does your body tense up?
- Does your mind go blank and wish the problem would just go away?
- Do you worry or panic?
- Do you feel overwhelmed by the force of the problem?

If you go through these or similar reactions of your body, mind or spirit, start directing comfort and love to each one. Through this gentle self-help, you will start to understand your reactions and feel more ordered mentally. And you will start to direct the interchange between your body and your mind.

As the everyday mind ceases to try to control your life, you will experience the unfolding of the purity and innocence that is within everyone.

7. Healing in its outer physical form is a subjective experience and the body may take longer than the mind to understand and manifest healing.

THE CYCLICAL NATURE OF BODY AND MIND

Tibetan medicine is acutely aware of the importance of the cyclical nature of emotional pain and how this cycle can be used to treat those suffering emotional disturbances and physical illness. All things in the body and mind work on monthly cycles influenced by the moon and the sun. Most are active at certain hours of the day and night, and are also associated with the phases of the moon. So conditions of the mind or body will respond to treatment at certain times of the night and day, in accordance with the body and mind's inner timing system.

We can tune into these cycles by doing a modern version of a traditional Tibetan practice. You will first need to find a calendar that shows you the four stages of the moon; these can often be found in New Age shops or, alternatively, some of the daily papers or magazines have astronomy or astrology columns that detail the lunar phases.

The ancient Tibetans believed that, on the days of new and full moons, lunar energy gathers in the back of your head where the head and neck meet. So, on these days, take some quiet time and start to tune in to your body. Evening or early morning is the best time, if possible, although any time will do. Focus your mind on that area at the base of your skull and feel the energies of the moon flowing with the tides of your heart, circulation and breathing.

This is a safe and simple meditation that puts you directly in touch with the cyclical energies of your body and mind. This preparation will help you do all the other meditations in this book.

PAINFUL HUMAN EXPERIENCES

According to the Tibetan belief, there are ten main categories of painful human experience. Every human being in every culture and society will go through these kinds of emotional pain in some way and at some time in their lives.

- Anxiety about having enough to live on
- Anxiety and stress about your physical safety, leading to a loss of ability to trust
- Excessive talking and fear of being alone with yourself, stemming from exhaustion
- Problems of addiction, or unskilful behaviour of any kind
- Emotional disturbance caused by environmental influences
- Problems with family and friends
- Recurrent bad dreams or nightmares, confusion with time

- Emotional pain concerned with violence
- Emotional pain resulting from the experience of physical pain
- Fear of death and dying

By exploring these ten key experiences, we can loosen the mind-made restrictions that encourage us to suffer and to be ill.

Tibetan medicine believes that negative or oppressive energies contain within them the essence of positive and liberating experiences. Simply, what makes you sick or fearful also has the potential to make you well and courageous. You need to turn the negative experience into a positive outcome and you can do this with the aid of the meditation exercises explained below.

Bearing in mind the seven principles I detailed earlier in this chapter, allow yourself to explore which of the areas of emotional pain affect you and then practise the relevant meditation. Always make yourself as comfortable as you can when you do these. Have a blanket nearby in case you suddenly get cold, and plenty of drinking water because you are likely to get thirsty.

Of course, it may be that none of the categories applies to you now, but at some time they will. Or they may be of use to other people in your life.

1. ANXIETY ABOUT HAVING ENOUGH TO LIVE ON

This is a universal fear, regardless of culture, time or place. According to Tibetan spirituality, it is one of the major causes of emotional disturbance and a strong contributor to physical ill-health. Many people who have great wealth worry in this way and it causes their inner natures to be starved of feelings of abundance, nourishment and safety. This is emotional poverty, a kind of spiritual virus which, like all forms of emotional disturbance, can be transmitted to other people.

Having this anxiety reduces vital life energy and makes you feel unhappy and isolated. And the more you worry about this, the more the worry acts as an obstacle to stop you from changing your situation.

The reason, perhaps, why people worry so much about this aspect of living is that they identify themselves with their belongings. Then they identify themselves without any and, more importantly, they iden-tify themselves with being out in the cold and starving to death. Incredible inner dramas are acted as people create fears which suffuse them with the belief that they deserve no better.

In this very moment, there are millions of people in the world in gruelling physical poverty and millions in extreme emotional poverty. Those in physical need can be helped but those in emotional need will find it harder to change.

Have you ever been weighed down in this way? Have you worried when the money would come? Whether you would have enough to pay the rent, the mortgage, the bills? It is a common experience.

For those of us on this small planet who are fortunate enough to have our bellies full every day, the inner poverty seems to grow the more we become seduced by our own comfort. Underneath most people's everyday minds lies a fear of losing what we have – job, house, lifestyle – and never regaining it. Then we become frightened.

This fear comes from a lack of inner connection to our own inner wisdom and our relationship with the natural world.

The material world will give you what you ask of it. Sometimes you will have to struggle to get what you have asked for. At other times, things come easily. Like the phases in an illness, one day you feel good, the next sick again. But there is a cure for this anxiety.

Meditation

The ancient Tibetans believed that you only gain something by giving up something else. So if you feel you have nothing, what do you give up? You give up the nothing you have.

Think about it. In your mind you are anxious about losing everything and having nothing. This means that in your thoughts you possess nothing, with a lot of emotional energy. So here is how you give it up.

Make yourself warm and sit in a comfortable position. Be quiet and breathe normally.

Let yourself feel the fears you have about your material world. As you feel each one, use your own words to give it up. Let it go. Give them all up to the world around you. Send them away with as much gentleness as you can.

Then tell them to come back to you only when they have become powerful, healing, abundance-making thoughts. In giving them up and demanding that they change, you send strong inner messages to yourself to start generating a new reality.

This meditation exercise is a simple version of what is called a 'ransom ritual' in Tibetan culture. You are exchanging negative energy for positive.

Rest in this state of mind, breathe it into you and think of it as water washing over you. Rest again. As you breathe in and then out, think of each breath as a gentle but penetrating flame burning away all the emotional garbage inside of you. Rest. Receive the returning positive energies.

Conditions helped by this meditation:
• Emotional: panic attacks, obsessive greed, jealousy, anger, depression, physical pain with no cause, hysteria, loneliness and lethargy.
• Physical: breathing difficulties, muscular spasms in the chest, stress-related disorders, respiratory and pulmonary problems, bleeding gums that don't respond to treatment, problem skin conditions, digestive disorders.

<~>

Jacob was an international criminal. He consulted me for a physical condition and ended up talking about his fear of poverty. He had grown up in the slums of a South American country, living on the streets, and scraping together anything he could to survive. Crime was his way out. He made a great deal of money and saw himself as a hero of the slums. But the money did not conquer his ingrained fear of poverty. He made more and more but still the fear was there. It took Jacob over two years of practising this meditation to overcome his profound insecurity. He put himself to the test by giving up crime and devoting the money he had made to help street children. Then he turned himself in to the police. Jacob has left prison now, and works in slums helping the children there.

<~>

2. FEAR FOR YOUR PHYSICAL SAFETY, LEADING TO A LOSS OF ABILITY TO TRUST

For many people the world is an unsafe place. They may live in war zones, experience horrific violations or see what they value destroyed. Then they forget the natural ability to trust. Regardless of what causes the fear, this is an experience which damages personal integrity and well-being, and causes deep ill-health and unhappiness.

If you have felt physically unsafe — even for a moment — you know how it feels not to be able to trust people and to think that the world is a bad place. Like the fear of not having enough material sustenance, it causes people to hide away from their potential and destroys creativity.

The world can overpower such vulnerable people. Having to deal with this constant anxiety can make them self-obsessed and prevent them from communicating openly with others. Most of us have experienced it to some degree: you can see it in the way you guard yourself against other people.

Healing this anxiety empowers you and gives you control over your world.

Meditation

Sit in an easy way with no strain on your body, or lie on your back. As you breathe in, imagine the breath is flowing in and out through your navel.

Think of the breath flowing to every part of you, and your body becoming warmer and more energetic. Then focus upon your physical heart. Imagine that in it lies an image of yourself where you are perfectly safe and free from all harm. Try to allow yourself to blend completely with this image.

Now use your mind to direct this image out into the everyday world around you. Allow it to radiate like sunlight into every corner of your life. Rest and let yourself receive the good feelings that come to you from doing this.

Conditions helped by this meditation:
- Emotional: speech impediments, communication problems, phobias of any kind including fear of open or closed spaces, of water or being underground.
- Physical: spinal and joint mobility problems, bladder infections, skin problems, discharges from the eyes.

<~>

Simon was a bodyguard, intelligent, tough and very dangerous. He routinely defended his clients from terrorists, assassins and snipers. His body was covered in scars and so was his mind. Deep inside, he felt scared — of physical violence and of how other people judged him. He trusted no one. Relationships foundered because he could not trust his girlfriends to trust him. Then a friend of his was seriously hurt on a job and Simon blamed himself. He fell to pieces. As he started to unravel his life with the help of this meditation he discovered that all his martial and psychological skills were defences to protect him from a frightening world. Slowly he let go his fears and found that he no longer wanted to work as a bodyguard. The former tough guy found he had a burning passion for flowers and started a florist business.

<~>

3. EXCESSIVE TALKING AND FEAR OF BEING ALONE STEMMING FROM EXHAUSTION

People who talk too much are a universal experience. Why do they do it? Because they are so incredibly tired and fatigued in mind and body that they do not know how to be in their own company if they stop talking and rest in silence.

They chat to cover up the exhaustion. But because they do not know how to stop being tired, or are afraid of admitting how tired they are, they feel themselves compressed into a small inner space. They are also afraid of spending time on their own and unable to acknowledge their own inner nature as a wonderful being.

Do you talk too much or get into cycles when your chatter goes into overdrive? Would you rather be with other people at all costs rather than spending time knowing who you are? Discovering your true self does not have to be an intense spiritual activity, it can be as simple as this meditation exercise. By integrating this into your daily life, you can experience the value of both speech and silence.

Meditation

Make yourself comfortable sitting on a chair with your hands on your lap. Close your eyes and breathe normally. Start to listen to all the sounds around you. Listen to them whether they are pleasant or not. Listen without prejudice. Treat them as your friends.

Each and every sound has something to offer you. Listen. Soon all the different sounds will merge together.

When this happens, breathe in and out slowly, imagining that the sounds are flowing into you, moving through your body and into your tongue and your brain, and then out into the world around you. Rest in the silence that comes from behind the sounds.

Conditions helped by this meditation:

- Emotional: fearfulness, a lack of self-esteem, a feeling that the world is grinding you down, or of being constantly overwhelmed.
- Physical: chronic illnesses of any kind, inner ear problems, tinnitus, sinus problems, influenza, skin conditions, structural problems of the lumbar spine, frozen shoulder.

<~>

Lara was a motor mouth. Nothing could stop her talking and while some of what she said was meaningful, most of it was rubbish. She told me that she talked all the time because she was afraid of what was inside her. Some people talk to cover up a vacuum but Lara felt there was something inside, some power, but it scared her so she covered it up by making a noise. As she did the meditation exercise above she began to feel connected to other people and to herself. She discovered that she was in fact very perceptive and had strong intuitive powers. Within a year she had changed into a person who only felt she had to speak when she had something to say. She now works as a counsellor to a local law enforcement authority and uses the meditation to help clients heal their exhausted minds.

<~>

4. PROBLEMS OF ADDICTION, AND UNSKILFUL BEHAVIOUR OF ANY KIND

Addiction and unskilful behaviour of any kind is the emotional fallout from a spiritual crisis. Whether the addict is chemically or psychologically addicted is the same, according to Tibetan medical teachings. Unskilful behaviour is any thought or action that causes you or someone else pain of any type. Addiction is its own pain and comes about because the person's soul is in a state of shock and disrepair. The emotional structures that enable the individual to live in the normal world have fallen apart because a great sense of separation and loss has been experienced. This may happen because of repeated unhappiness of any type that creates damage within the person so that they feel unable to make sense of themselves, the reality they inhabit, or the rest of the world.

Many addicts are highly spiritually developed, but never had the chance to fully develop their inner wisdom. It's as though their minds and bodies cannot handle their inner spiritual awareness so that they quite simply crack open. And they feel that, like Humpty Dumpty, they can never be put together again.

Addicts use their addiction to avoid confronting their true feelings. This results in a kind of automatic response being set up where they use the same emotional patterns in all circumstances. So an alcoholic, for example, would use the pain of dealing with everyday life as a reason for drinking – anything from a row with a loved one to problems at work. There would always be a justification. The alcohol would apparently hide the pain but would, in fact, just transform it into an emotional fuel to drive the alcoholic through another day.

Meditation that enables the pain to heal is a crucial part of a larger recovery process. This exercise empowers the desire to heal the emotional pain coming from addiction and creates a sense of well-being. It helps people to come to terms with the fact that they have an addictive illness, and is also beneficial for those suffering a terminal illness.

Meditation

Lie on your back, stretch out and breathe normally. Focus on your physical heart and listen to your heartbeat.

Now focus on your addiction. See your addiction pulsing through you in time with the beat of your heart. Through the beat feel the outer limits of your physical body. See how your addiction and your body react to each other. Breathe this in and out.

Direct as much love as you can to the reaction between your body and the addiction. Remember that although your addiction is a spiritual crisis, it is played out within your body through your emotional energy. Now be as still as you can.

Feel the love you created. Receive as best you can the feelings that you experience as a result of this exercise.

Conditions helped by this meditation:

- Emotional: total despair, a desire for suicide or violent behaviour to oneself or others, sudden fits of crying or rage, obsessions with negative experiences.
- Physical: eases the physical pain of nerve damage or a terminal illness; encourages the body to rest and allows a better chance for the body's healing systems to work; may help circulatory, elimination and digestive functions; helps stop or reduce stress headaches.

<~>

Darryl was an addict of epic proportions. He was unable to resist alcohol, drugs, sex, shopping and his own ego. He tried to give up many times and failed. Partly because he was also addicted to being an addict – it became his raison d'être. He told me that he did really want to give up, but just didn't know how. He felt powerless. Although, like all addicts, he behaved as if he cared nothing for others, in fact he was extraordinarily perceptive about them. And what he felt hurt him so much that he fell back into his addictions. As he used the meditation, he noticed that he was less affected by other people and by the world around him. He felt strong enough to go to his therapist regularly and attend a support group, both of which helped him to deal with the causes of his addiction. He is happier today and works as a therapist.

<~>

5. EMOTIONAL DISTURBANCE CAUSED BY ENVIRONMENTAL INFLUENCES

Environmental influences can cause damage in several ways. Being oppressed either by land or buildings can lead to emotional disturbance. Physical illness can result from ingesting toxins in earth, water, plants, gases or other naturally occurring substances. Additionally, a person's mind and emotions may become disturbed by the influences of weather, light, wind and seasonal variations. The Tibetans believe that many people can be adversely influenced in this manner, and that their personalities then take on the prevailing emotional influences created by other people around them.

Cities are regarded as potential sources of emotional pollution because they hold huge amounts of thoughts, ideas and energies that can cause people to become confused and increase stress and negative behaviour. The way buildings are planned also affects emotional health. Because cities are normally a jumble of conflicting architectural styles they can block energetic flow.

Certain alignments of natural landscapes can also affect some people's emotional health. Living close to rivers or oceans, for example, can influence stability.

Sometimes a move may be the only solution, but the meditation exercise below can help you to become more balanced and be less influenced by the surrounding environment.

Meditation

Make sure you are warm, then lie down on your back. Breathe in and out slowly, as deeply as you can but in your normal manner. Slowly think about how your environment influences you. As you do this, sing the sound '*Ahh*' over and over again at a deep pitch. Do this quietly at first, then progressively louder.

Imagine that the sound is starting to flow out to every part of your environment, transforming all the negativity and in its place creating a positive healing force that flows back into you so that the environment can no longer influence you. As the positive force flows back to you, imagine that your body and mind start to become full of clear sparkling energy. Rest. Then send this energy back out to the surrounding environment.

Think of everything around you – people, land and buildings – becoming blessed with overwhelming joy and love. Rest, then send this energy back into the surrounding environment. Once again, think of everything around you – people, land and buildings – becoming blessed with overwhelming joy and love. Receive this, too, and bless yourself.

Then send this blessing out into the environment and let it go: do not expect to have it back. Be selfless.

Conditions helped by this meditation:
- Emotional: feeling overwhelmed by your environment in a negative, brooding way; feeling that you have no energy left to do anything – even thinking is too much; feeling sad without knowing why; feeling that you cannot trust, love or laugh any more.
- Physical: stomach pains, joint pains, circulatory problems, infectious and viral illnesses, the aftermath of food poisoning, illnesses caused by any type of parasites, the effects of bites from poisonous animals, following orthodox medical treatment.

<~>

Geoff lived in the centre of one of the world's biggest cities. His senses were dominated by noise, pollution, steel and glass. The only time he experienced silence and peace was in his 24th-floor apartment. Although he was a successful writer, counsellor and self-help trainer, he felt exhausted by the city and its noise and tensions. Just walking among the milling crowds jarred his nerves and drained his energy. He started to feel burnt out and withdrawn. At first he thought he was having a breakdown, then he understood that he was suffering from emotional and environmental pollution. The energies of other people and his environment were causing him to lose little pieces of himself. The force of the city and its repressed emotional energies were making him into someone else.

He started to practise the meditation exercise above and within a few months he became more balanced and less influenced by his environment. He also understood that, in his desire to help others and be successful in his career, he had not developed enough inner resources to deal with all the demands that others placed on him, and that he placed on himself. He realised that his physical environment mirrored the way he was feeling. His apartment lay in the shadow of a much taller building and was constantly in half light and half dark. Just as he felt.

Geoff had always believed he could only follow his career in the city, but he decided to move to nearby countryside. He found that he started to respond to people differently and his clients treated him with new respect. Not only did he feel completely restored but, to his amazement, he was even more successful.

<~>

6. PROBLEMS WITH FAMILY AND FRIENDS

Virtually all of us have suffered from emotional pain caused by friends or family. There are three types of emotional pain that are common, whatever the culture or circumstance:

- Recurrent emotional pain caused by a betrayal of trust.
- Emotional pain caused by loneliness and abandonment.
- Emotional pain caused by dominating personalities.

The following meditation will help to heal the wounds.

Meditation

Lie on your back and focus on your body. Feel your physical body and relax into it. Feel its shape, contours, weight. Feel how heavy you can be. Feel how long your body is, and how strong.

Sense the clear, vibrant energy flowing into your body. Now remember every important person in your life and direct this energy to them. It purifies them, and removes their pain, fear and insecurity. It makes them happy.

Now feel all your inner pain starting to melt away as a result of your good thoughts. Slowly you feel more capable and more aware of what is important in your life. Direct these good thoughts out into the world.

Conditions helped by this meditation:

- Emotional: feelings of not being paid enough attention, of abandonment and of being unable to show affection; an overwhelming fear of childbirth, fears of sexual intimacy, of being alone, or of touch.
- Physical: extreme skin conditions, boils, cuts and wounds, preparing for and recovering from major surgery, terminal illness.

<~>

Shara was afraid of everything. Since childhood, she had lived with all the sorts of emotional pain I've described above. Her family had effectively abandoned her – they were, in her words, more interested in TV than in her – and she was left to wander the streets. Her conviction that she was stupid and the belief that no one cared for her dominated her life. She became involved with prostitution, drugs and crime. Curiously, it was a television programme that started her journey out of her personal hell. It described the lives of people in her situation and motivated her to go and get the education she had never had. During this process Shara also learned about herself and realised that, despite the strides she had made, she was still a mess inside. A friend introduced her to me and she started the meditation exercise. As she practised it, she gained great insight into her situation. Her emotional strength grew and her mind became more alive. She consulted a psychotherapist regularly, and this led to her feeling that she could start the process of forgiving her family. Eventually Shara persuaded her parents and her siblings to practise the meditation with her. The chasm between them began to close.

<~>

7. RECURRENT BAD DREAMS OR NIGHTMARES, CONFUSION WITH TIME

This type of emotional pain relates to when we become confused or shocked, perplexed or blocked by recurrent dreams whose meanings seem to escape us. It also relates to being frightened by nightmares, or the sense of being in a dreamlike state when we are awake, with never enough time to do anything.

The Tibetans believe that dreams hold important spiritual meanings for us and that the reason we dream is to maintain mental sanity and clarity. It is the everyday mind's way of clearing out emotional garbage, gaining self-knowledge and being able to know our true inner mind.

According to Tibetan tradition, our dreams can be cultivated so that we can enter into our dream state and discover the sources both of our illusions, delusions, inspirations and insights. Dreaming is essential in regulating the underlying cycles of health, and this meditation can help to solve problems associated with it.

Meditation

Go to bed one hour before you normally do. As you relax, think of a milky-white glowing light beginning to flood through your mind and all your thoughts. All you think and feel and see within is this milky whiteness. Time has no place: you understand that it is artificial.

Focus on a recurring dream or nightmare. As you start to feel or see it, let it start to dissolve into the milky whiteness. Allow a great feeling of peace to flow through you. Time washes away like paint in water.

Out of the whiteness comes the true meaning or indication of your dream or nightmare. You are freed of time. Let it go.

Sleep and you will start to discover a new way of dreaming.

Conditions helped by this meditation:
• Emotional: feeling emotionally stuck, unable to make decisions or speak clearly; feeling controlled by time and all its associated experiences and problems.
• Physical: difficulty in waking, poor vision and smell, hair loss, weight

problems, sore throats, rheumatic conditions, bladder and liver problems, minor glandular problems and wasting muscles; it can also help the well-being of patients with osteoarthritis, metastatic tumours, lymphoma (cancers of the lymph system) and Paget's disease (a chronic bone-wasting condition).

<~>

Every night, John, a soldier who had seen active duty in war zones, would dream of a young child who was crying silently. All around there were scenes of war and pestilence, famine and disease. The child would start to radiate light and fly on angelic wings over the dead and dying, sprinkling water over them in a blessing.

John would wake in tears and in physical pain. All he could think about was the dream. Paradoxically, he felt as if his everyday life was a dream. When he started to do the meditation he became more open and aware of conflicts between his inner self and his job. As he spoke to me about it, he realised that his inner spirit was calling him to face the anguish and horror of what he had witnessed during his active service. He felt a rising conflict between his spiritual needs and his life in the armed forces. Then, as he was going through old photographs one day, he saw the face of the child in his dream. It was him as a young child.

Suddenly John knew what he must do. Despite scorn from some of his colleagues, he trained as a chaplain, tending to the spiritual needs of people in the armed forces. He became a spiritually empowered person who, through his own experience, was able to bring spiritual insight into the lives of those who wanted it.

<~>

8. EMOTIONAL PAIN CONCERNED WITH VIOLENCE

Violence is a state of active confusion that seeks to control forces beyond it. We are talking here about violent feelings in your own mind, about violent action that you take against others or is taken against you.

Violence is based not on anger but on greed. Greed wants to control, separate and divide. Violence destroys what is around it and also destroys the originator. But violence and greed are part of ourselves, an essential activating energy that can be transformed. Greed seeks to be listened to before it will transform itself into positive energy; violence seeks only to be acknowledged by all those involved in the violent act so that it may transmute into love and wisdom.

Emotional pain caused by violence is a form of energetic injury, a spiritual bruising, which can be healed by meditation.

Meditation

Lie on your back and relax. Focus your mind on your belly. Feel yourself becoming physically stronger. Rest in this sensation and allow it to flow all over your body.

Focus upon the emotional pain caused by violence. Direct the physical sensations of strength into your pain and let it start to dissolve. In its place see a deep copper red light flow all over your body and flood into your mind. This light cascades into your physical heart, which pumps it through your veins with your blood, into your body, bones and brain.

Rest in this state for as long as you are able.

Conditions helped by this meditation:

- Emotional: releasing the experience of reliving a physical trauma; sudden negative thoughts that come out of nowhere.
- Physical: muscle damage and general mobility of the upper body.

> Dorothy, a doctor, came to see me because she had experienced violence first hand and felt she could not continue living. She had worked with child prostitutes, pimps, drug dealers and other dangerous people in a poverty-stricken area of a large city.
>
> She was caught up in a riot that flared when the police raided someone's house. Caught in the cross fire, she was shot in the chest and legs. As she tried to get up, she was stabbed repeatedly and had her jaw and arm broken. It was only a friend who lived in the slum who convinced the police to take her to hospital.
>
> Dorothy was much respected and both sides apologised after they realised who she was, but the harm had been done. Her body had taken on the injury and the pain. She gave up her work in the city and practised in a quieter area. But the violence continued inside her.
>
> She felt so traumatised that she cut herself off from her husband and children. She was afraid to go out by herself and she wanted to stop being a doctor. She couldn't understand why it had all happened to her. She felt angry, powerless and violated.
>
> Dorothy learned the meditation and bit by bit her shock began to heal. It also helped the constant pain from her injuries. An excellent psychotherapist, who

encouraged her to continue the meditation, also helped,
and she was eventually able to forgive those who had
hurt her. The last I heard of her she was still prac-
tising medicine and had felt secure enough to visit the
slum where the violence had taken place.

<~>

9. EMOTIONAL PAIN THAT COMES FROM EXPERIENCING PHYSICAL PAIN

Extreme or constant physical pain can cause our emotions to close down and restrict the process of healing or recovery. The emotional pain is experienced as stress, worry, anxiety or other forms of emotional restriction. It serves only to prolong any type of physical pain, thus creating a vicious cycle. The emotional pain becomes harder and harder to deal with because it is just the tip of whatever other kind of pain you are experiencing.

Meditation

Sit as comfortably as you can. Listen to your breathing and follow your breath as it flows in and out; focus on the short natural pause between the in and out breath.

As you breathe in, feel huge amounts of powerful positive energy flowing into every part of you, softening your pain, and reducing its intensity. As you breathe out, let your pain flow out, leaving your body soft and warm.

With every breath in and out, feel your pain reduce and your body increase in mobility and warmth. Warmth flows everywhere in your mind and body. Gently it turns into a radiant sky-blue, and your body and mind is flooded with this sparkling sky-blue light. Your physical pain is released.

Now rest and give goodness to all living creatures so that they too can reduce their pain.

Conditions helped by this meditation:
- Emotional: seeing beyond the experience of pain to understanding its nature, why you have it and that you can control or manage it; fear caused by pain.
- Physical conditions: extreme oversensitivity in nerve damage; regulates uneven breathing, so helping pain levels; helps digestion and excretion.

Sam had been in constant pain all his life because of nerve damage from a childhood car crash. Depression and mood swings were his everyday state. For a time, he was addicted to painkillers. His physical pain fuelled his emotional pain and his suffering became progressively more intense. Normal relationships with other people were difficult because the pain made his body twitch and he felt like a freak. His emotions became frozen and he started to hate the world and to withdraw from people. A friend explained this meditation to Sam and also encouraged him to come and see me. As Sam learned the meditation, he started to let go of the emotions that the pain had trapped in his body and mind through the years. Feelings came back to his mind and, as they did so, the physical pain lessened. Today, the pain has greatly improved with the effect of the meditation. He still uses it regularly to help his body and mind move towards knowing his inner wisdom.

<~>

10. FEAR OF DEATH AND DYING

According to Tibetan teachings, death does not happen in the way we think it does in the West – dying does. Our bodies cease, but our inner nature continues on. Life after life, the qualities of our inner nature adapt to the differing experiences of each life, in much the same way as our minds adapt to each circumstance in this life.

The Tibetans teach that fears surrounding death and dying stem from fears about what we may discover about ourselves as we go through the death experience.

Understanding the brevity of physical life is good because it helps you to respect your mind and your body, and also other people. But a lot of people flash from one life to another without realising that they go through the process of dying. As in life, they rush through, without cherishing or knowing it. The fear of death and dying comes because you are in some way aware of the process within you, but have not accepted it.

When fears about death get out of hand, it is because the person concerned has some insight into their spiritual nature, which heightens their awareness of impermanence. Such people are often psychic, empathic or highly intuitive, and also acutely aware of other people's suffering. But because their minds are not trained to deal with this awareness, they can become confused and unable to make sense of their own life.

This meditation exercise will help to still the conflict.

Meditation

This exercise shows you the life-giving energy behind the nature of death. It also slightly mimics what people experience when they die.

Be as still as you can. Let your breathing slow down. Imagine that all your senses, thoughts and feelings can pick up and see everything around you. You may feel a little overwhelmed. Do not worry. Be at peace.

You can sense a clear sparkling light flowing round you. Imagine you want to speak to those who care for you, but they can't hear your voice. You feel as if you're in a fast-moving river, being jostled about. You get near the edge of a waterfall and fear you may fall over, but you don't. You stay safely on the edge, suspended in space.

You start to become aware of just how many people are being born and dying in this very moment. All you sense is joy and happiness. There is no fear.

Relax into this feeling and receive its energy. You see a clear light come towards you. Enter into it without doubt and stay there for as long as you can.

When you leave the light, rest and give thanks for all parts of nature and life. Send love and goodness to all life.

Conditions helped by this meditation:
- Emotional: the need always to be in control, arrogance, the effects of gossip on both the gossiper and the person talked about, the inability to share emotions, money or insight, doubts about loving and love, fear of finding out who you are and of living the life that is true for you, fear of taking responsibility for your life, fear of growing up, fear that at death there is nothing else.
- Physical: problems of the neck and spinal structure of the neck, problems of the jaw and upper and lower palate; thrombosis, angina, cardiac conditions, hernias, vomiting, problems following exposure to severe elements; helpful after transplants and in easing shock, or injury to the head.

<~>

Dan was a Catholic priest who also worked as a psychotherapist. When I met him, he was going through a crisis of faith because he had discovered he was afraid of death and dying. He tried to deal with his fear by exerting a fierce control over his life. The repercussions had started to contaminate his emotions and his relationships, and to affect his body – his jaw became rigid and very sore and his back tensed up and caused him pain. As the fear got worse, Dan lost all his connection with living: life was something that happened to other people. A close friend told Dan that he had become callous and uncaring towards him and others. This shocked him profoundly.

His whole life was meant to be dedicated to caring for others and serving his God – the God who had conquered death. When we met, Dan felt he was powerless to do anything – carry out his work, connect with the divine, and even walk or listen to music. He was isolated and lonely.

Practising this meditation slowly reconnected him to life, and he began to understand that life includes death. He began to feel the stirrings of his faith being reborn, and he started to study death and dying as part of his work. This enabled him to become a whole person and he felt equipped to help others to heal their own fears. He uses the meditation as a form of prayer to help him communicate with his God, his source of eternal life.

Dan discovered that, for him, coming to terms with death was the doorway to the meaning of life.

<~>

Reflect on this chapter in quiet. Learn how your inner self is responding to the exercises. You will find they will improve your sense of harmony and well-being.

You can use these meditations for other people, but be absolutely sure that they want to receive such energies. If possible, ask them directly.

To do the exercises for someone else, think of the person and then do the meditation.

These are powerful healing exercises, so use them with discernment. Every good thought misdirected has an effect somewhere in the world that may be undesirable.

CHAPTER SIX
The Three Humours

*T*he concept of the three humours is at the heart of the operating system of Tibetan medicine. Physicians categorise people into three humoural types: Wind (*rlung*), Bile (*mkhris pa*) and Phlegm (*bad kan*). Physicians see the humours as energetic forces with different characteristics, moving through your body and mind and out into the universe.

- Wind is a clear, sparkling, colourless stream of energy that can be quick or slow or completely still, all at the same time.
- Bile is a dark red-brown bubbling energy, like lava, which is dense yet taut and fast-moving.
- Phlegm is a deep, laid-back, blue-green force which is reflective and very slow-moving.

According to Tibetan medicine, the three humours are the basis of all our experiences, from the time of our conception to our physical death. They govern every aspect of how the body and mind function, create structures and talk to each other. They are implicit in all our emotional, intellectual, spiritual and physical dynamics. They are the centres of our minds and form the embodiment of our personalities. They hold the abundance of who we can be. They can reveal the deepest workings of our own consciousness, both as individuals and as members of the human species. We are never separated from them: as we are born, die, and recycled in the natural world, so are the three humours.

They interact in this way:
- Wind is the motivating force and life energy of the others, but it cannot act harmoniously without them;
- Wind increases the intensity of the Bile humour's influence;
- Wind gives Phlegm movement and adaptability and enhances its supportive functions in the body;

- Bile stimulates the activity of Wind;
- Bile delivers warmth and action to Phlegm;
- Phlegm can relax Bile.

Each and every human endeavour is created, continued and destroyed by the dynamic flow of the humours. Like three great currents moving through all humankind, these forces are the origins of our cultural and psychological identities. In a state of balance, they sweep us towards higher thought and actions. Out of balance, they drive us into nightmares of negative and catastrophic activity. By learning to know your humoural nature and harmonising it, you contribute to the harmony of the world.

We are predominantly one humoural type, or a combination of two – the first dominant and the second subdominant. But all three humours are within each of us and the aim is to achieve balance, so that they work together to create well-being and prevent ill-health. Although people are far more complex than this kind of typing may suggest, categorising them in this way helps Tibetan medicine explain how illness expresses itself in individuals, and how they experience well-being.

Illness occurs when our dominant humour (and/or the subdominant humour, if we have one) is out of balance. This happens principally through lifestyle problems, including stress, poor diet, and pollution, which make us susceptible to diseases of different types, from colds to cancer.

Health is based on balancing the humours. By understanding how they adapt, react and condition their environment – that is, you – you will become more aware of how you create patterns that reduce well-being and lead to illness, and the reverse. This process can take place on many inner levels, connected to many everyday experiences.

THE ORIGINS OF THE THREE HUMOURS

Tibetan Bön legend ascribes the origins of the theory to the first inhabitants of the earth — non-human beings who are known as the 18 brothers and sisters of existence. Medical anthropologists and experts on Tibetan culture believe it travelled with traders and migrating peoples into Tibet and the Himalayan region from Central Asia in the 9th century BC or even earlier.

It permeated into Tibet and the Himalayan region, eventually finding its way into the Indian subcontinent to influence Vedic beliefs, and then Hinduism and the Indian medical system known as Ayurveda. The theory then returned to Tibet in the 7th and 8th centuries AD with the arrival of Indian Buddhist missionaries.

The three humours are also reflected in the Western theory of the four cardinal humours. Hippocrates, a doctor working on the Greek island of Cos, in the early 5th century AD, put forward the theory that the body had four humours, which were the chief fluids of the body: black bile (also known as melancholy or black choler), yellow bile (or choler), blood and phlegm. This signalled a new approach to medicine as a natural science; baleful deities had formerly been held responsible for illness and disease. It's likely that Hippocrates based his belief on the system of the three humours.

The expression of the three humours is inextricably entwined with the concept of the five elements — Earth, Water, Fire, Wind/Air and Space — which are in all aspects of consciousness, mental, psychological, physical and intellectual. The humours are the result of how the elements interact with each other.

THE NATURE OF ILLNESS

Tibetan medicine believes in a strong psychosomatic relationship in many forms of illness. Why? Because, simply put, your life, my life, all our lives, day in and day out, are a psychosomatic experience. Our psychological nature interacts with the physical world, each affecting the other and creating a continuous new experience which adds up to the quality of our daily living.

The Tibetans claim that we are born, not brand new as we believe in the West, but already one year old. Before our first breath, we have been conditioned by our psychosomatic experiences in the womb. There we have experienced the world through our own senses of taste and hearing, even sight, so we come into each physical life with certain qualities and habits already influencing our behaviour. Some of our basic humoural tendencies are already formed, crucially the way we respond to illness and health.

Tibetan medicine regards illness as an obstruction. Obstructions decrease valuable life energy. If you have a problem that will not go away, or one that continually repeats itself, an obstruction is at the root. What this means is that you have the potential to suffer an illness because the three humours have become damaged and will start to throw the body and mind out of balance.

Taking this one step further, Tibetans see problems that affect our minds in the way we think of a physical complaint. The damage mental problems cause to our well-being is the same as a physical wound. To heal this trauma and create well-being, we have to cultivate good attitudes that increase the quantities of physical and mental energies available to us.

The humours are seen as the foundations of anger, lust and greed (the origins of the eight material activities, as I described in Chapter 4). Ignorance of why and how we suffer lulls us into becoming trapped by these three unskilful emotions. This mental ignorance is the basic cause of suffering and of all bodily illnesses, according to Tibetan medicine.

The body is more than blood, muscle, bone and nerve; it is an extension of your material mind in the everyday world. To become a whole person – mentally, physically, emotionally and spiritually – you must try to heal your ignorance by caring for the three humours.

As we improve our attitudes – reducing our anger, lust and greed – so our humoural balance improves. The Tibetan view of the healthy individual is someone who can balance the ups and downs of everyday life in such a way that good energy comes in a spontaneous manner.

Well-being and illness are basically the same process, but expressed differently. One can be born from the other. Every day, our minds take in a series of experiences. The way in which our minds and bodies respond to those experiences directs our health. But we have the ability to transform obstructions. If, for example, we encounter problems at every turn but manage to focus on the creation of good energy, the obstruction loses its bite. So we do not become ill.

At the end of this chapter there are self-healing exercises to help you to overcome the sort of obstructions we all meet in everyday life.

IDENTIFYING AND LOOKING AFTER YOUR HUMOURAL TYPE

The theory of the three humours is very complex. If you went to a physician of Tibetan medicine, you would be asked a range of 29 comprehensive questions to diagnose humoural imbalances; depending on your answers the physician would prescribe remedies. I have simplified this advice here to enable you to understand the emotional and psychological aspects of each of the humours and to initiate your own simple self-healing programme. In Chapter 8, which deals with food and nutrition, you will find more about the medical aspects of the three humours.

The sections below will enable you to learn about the general attributes of the three humours, to identify your dominant humour (or combination of dominant and subdominant humours), to investigate any imbalances and to restore health using the ancient Tibetan wisdom of seasonal healing, which connects you to the cycles of nature through food, environment and lifestyle. Don't mix up the seasonal activities or you risk more imbalance: they are quite specific to that humour and that season.

You may find that you have a dominant and a subdominant humour; in this case, follow the seasonal activities for your dominant humour. Later, when your dominant humour is balanced, you can begin to work on your subdominant humour.

Understanding the three humours will help you to become more loving, powerful and generous, to grow a little wiser and not to take yourself as seriously as society would sometimes have you do. Let your heart be open and your mind clear and discerning so that you may discover the enlightenment that is to be found in the miracle of daily life.

GENERAL GUIDELINES FOR MAINTAINING HUMOURAL BALANCE

1. Always follow your inner voice, otherwise known as 'intuition', about situations and people.

2. When you are in good health, always eat and drink what you intuitively feel is right for you. Exercise as much as you want, whether that is a little or a lot.

3. Respect other people and life forms.

4. Be as good as you can and do not do anything you believe to be wrong.

5. Follow an occupation that is in accordance with what you truly want and need; personal satisfaction is the best medicine for keeping your humours balanced.

GENERAL FACTORS THAT UNBALANCE THE HUMOURS:

1. Eating food that disagrees with you in any way; for instance, making you feel heavy or sluggish, bloated or otherwise uncomfortable.

2. Not giving yourself enough rest and sleep at appropriate times.

3. Not respecting your body and/or mind, whether this is taking them for granted or more actively holding them in contempt.

4. Undergoing continual stress that causes changes in your behaviour or personality.

5. Acting or behaving in a way that causes you shame or embarrassment, or brings hurt to others.

<~>

The nature of Wind humour

The workings of the Wind humour, which is situated in the centre of the body, are not always easy to see. Wind is affected by your thought processes, the way the central nervous system communicates with your physical body, and how all the sensory organs perceive and interpret knowledge and relay it back to your brain.

For instance, the way in which your skin, your largest organ, works to protect you against the environment and how it acts as a conduit for sensation, is a Wind function.

The Wind humour also influences your breathing, heart rate, speech patterns, and general energy levels. It is associated with greed, melancholy and a sort of depression that causes people to lose touch with the world.

If unbalanced, Wind like Bile (see below) can speed up the process of illness. Stress and negative patterns can impel Wind and Bile to rise, which leads to shortness of breath, shock or trauma or skin eruptions, or to descend, causing cramps or problems with intestines, pancreas, liver or gall bladder.

Wind shows its effects in the body and mind through dryness and lightness. Wind-dominant people tend to have bony angular bodies, sometimes crooked looking. There is thinness about them and a very slight bluish tint to their overall complexion. Their joints can crack or seem a little stiff when moving. They catch colds or chills easily. They love to sing and argue, enjoy dangerous situations and taking risks, and need drama of any type in their lives. They can be extremely senti-mental and naïve. They like bitter and sour foods and enjoy strong alcoholic drinks.

All children, from birth up to eleven years old, are Wind types. After 11, they separate into the different categories of humour, some staying as Wind types. Wind adults may be very spiritual and apparently happy, yet also depressed at the same time. They teeter on a tightrope. A Wind person whose humour is balanced would, for example, help people without wanting reward or recognition.

Wind people can improve their self-healing capacity by developing mental clarity through meditation or simply stopping and contemplating. This will help them to get in touch with the knowledge that is a powerful resource of energy, both physical and mental, deep inside them. Everything they need is there, just waiting to be discovered.

People who are predominantly Wind with a subdominant Bile are short and often squat as the two humours together create a powerful interaction and dynamic tension so that the height and thinness of the pure Wind type goes and the emphatic energy of the Bile humour takes over. Wind/Bile types have a tendency to be very fixed on ambition and success. This humoural combination makes natural teachers and negotiators. They are peace-makers who are often seen as exemplars of human potential.

People who add Phlegm to a dominant Wind humour may be shy, but also tend to be curious about everything. Adults with this combination tend to be small and very much connected to the natural forces of the earth. There is sometimes a slight golden tint to their hands and feet, while the rest of their skin is light toned.

A person with a Wind imbalance is the type who always pesters you at parties, talking about themselves and becoming upset when you leave, or the type who asks you for money at airports or when you go shopping. Busybodies, gossips and religious fanatics also come into this category, as well as most politicians because they deal in ideas and talk with very little physical manifestation.

In society, television and associated media, computer software and the Internet are good examples of the Wind humour. They work with unseen energy and communicate with a technology of which the essence is invisible to the human eye, but which permeates into every culture in the world.

CHARACTERISTICS OF BEING IN BALANCE

Wind types are full of energy when they are in balance, highly intuitive and very willing to help others. They have lithe, strong, supple bodies which they fuel with their preferred diet of fresh fruit and vegetables, plus a little meat and dairy food. They are enchanted by music and dance and are happiest when exploring their spiritual potential.

Wind/Bile personalities share the same characteristics as Wind types when in balance, but are more introvert, with sudden bursts of energy that are highly directed and focused.

Wind/Phlegm types find harmony by immersing themselves in the natural world. Quiet and gentle when in balance, they have a great capacity for understanding the forces of nature and communicating this to others. They understand the natural energy of the planet and are good with plants and animals.

SYMPTOMS OF WIND IMBALANCE

Wind: sleep problems, dislike of exposed environments, anxiety for no obvious reason, general unhappiness, joint pains, involuntary twitching, muscle-wasting, neurological problems such as Parkinson's disease and dementia, breathing problems, pins and needles, sudden bursts of fatigue or energy, and cravings for food, alcohol, drugs or people.

Wind/Bile: as above, but singly. When out of balance, this combination of humours has a tendency to manifest single symptoms, physical or emotional, that come on suddenly and last only a short time, leaving the Wind/Bile person exhausted.

Wind/Phlegm: as Wind, but in a slow lingering manner; when out of balance Wind/Phlegm types become ill very slowly and may have no idea that they have an underlying disease.

Spring: Drink fresh juices at room temperature in the morning. Drink small amounts of dark beer with roasted root vegetables and dark meat or oily fish. Spend time looking at the new growth around you and, if you can, work in a garden or on a farm. Massage your feet, legs, hands, fingers and arms for 20 minutes twice daily; avoid afternoon naps, but do go to bed early.

Summer: Sunbathe for one hour in the afternoon. Take long, warm baths twice daily for half an hour each time. Choose peaceful surroundings and supportive friends. Drink freshly made vegetable and fruit juices for breakfast. Avoid eating salads raw – instead, poach vegetables lightly or wilt leaves. Eat roasted root vegetables. Avoid meat, coffee, tea, alcohol, puddings and confectionery.

Autumn: Spend time near running water. Listen to soft music, books read aloud, and the sound of children's laughter (or teenagers or adults who are young at heart). Eat little and often and avoid sweet food and alcohol.

Winter: Play with happy children and healthy dogs. Sit in contemplation near an open fire, but don't get too hot. Burn incense with a calming aroma, such as sandalwood, myrrh, frankincense, jasmine or any Tibetan incense. Eat warming comfort foods, such as soups and stews, but avoid over-sweet or spicy dishes. Evening meals with high fat food, accompanied by dark beer, are beneficial. Massage your entire body gently and firmly for 20 minutes when you wake and at bedtime, using sesame seed oil, clarified butter (*ghee*), or any thick vegetable oil.

The nature of Bile humour

This is the heating humour, located to the left of the body, which stimulates digestion and immune functions and controls heart rate, digestion, respiration and the excretory process, among other bodily functions. Bodily reflexes are also controlled by Bile.

This humour influences anger and also laughter. Bile people have a tendency to be cranky and annoyed by small things, also impatient with an urge to get things done now, or preferably yesterday. An imbalance can accentuate this attitude.

Bile-dominant people have strong appetites and get hungry and thirsty frequently. There is a very slight redness or light yellow tint to their complexions. They are normally acutely intelligent, with a tendency towards mysticism, and may be egotistical and quietly proud.

Bile types with a Phlegm subdominance are normally tall, bony and nervous because the two humours are in a love/hate relationship, with Bile constantly overheating the damp of the Phlegm, while Phlegm is trying to cool down the ardour of the Bile.

In the same way as Wind (see above), Bile can speed up the process of illness. Bile-dominant people are very aware of their individuality. Any type of over-activity, including extreme attitudes and obsessions, increases bile imbalance. This can be generated by violent energies, such as severe hate, anger or extreme emotional upset.

CHARACTERISTICS OF BEING IN BALANCE

When balanced, Bile types are highly active, and deep and profound thinkers who make natural leaders. They have great endurance and stamina; sport and challenging activities are a crucial part of their lifestyle. They are powerfully interested in the opposite sex. They love meats and spicy foods, and tend to eat little and often. They like reading, researching and debating issues, and are capable of inspiring others to be passionate about life.

Bile/Wind types in balance seek to right wrongs and help the down- trodden; they are deeply connected to the ideas of justice, human rights, equality and freedom for all – this becomes their raison d'être and they are very good at organising and motivating other people.

When balanced, Bile/Phlegm combinations imbue everyone they meet with a sense of safety and security; they understand the impor- tance of nurturing and of laying down roots and are excellent at creating homes, balanced families and communities; they are storytellers and keepers of family histories; they remember the past and pass it on with insight; they are the keepers of family and community records and heir- looms.

On the positive side, Bile people often use their impressive personal wisdom to benefit others. For example, a Bile person would have no hesitation in saving someone's life without regard for his or her own safety. All emergency services are typically influenced by Bile, also natural events such as sudden earthquake, tidal wave, lightning and thunderstorm or the outbreak of war.

The effects of Bile on the mind and body can be pervasive and penetrating, and are felt in every part of a person's life, from mind and body to daily living.

SYMPTOMS OF BILE IMBALANCE

Bile: stomach pains, back problems, digestive disorders, constipation, feeling of tiredness just after eating or drinking, recurrent infections or injuries, sexually transmitted diseases, blood disorders, sudden bouts of anger, recurrent bad dreams that cause physical reactions such as waking in a state of alarm, sweating or shouting out loud, and sleep- walking.

Bile/Wind: as above, but this combination experiences short sharp symptoms that come and go quickly.

Bile/Phlegm: as above, but the symptoms will have a slow onset, become intense, and then linger.

HOW TO HEAL BILE IMBALANCES ACCORDING TO THE SEASONS

Spring: Aim for light food, bland and nutritious, such as soups and broths with weak black tea in the evening, but no coffee. A calm environment is essential, preferably near trees; if this is impossible, pin up photos of mountains and lakes and watch Nature programmes on TV. Direct but gentle conversations are important. Massage the upper torso and joints twice daily for 20 minutes, on waking and before bed, using an invigorating strong-smelling oil or balm.

Summer: Again light food is important to balance unbalanced bile. Encourage friendly but honest conversations. Try doing puzzles and crosswords and playing cards or board games – gamble if you wish, but not with money. Do good things for other people and read books that make you feel better spiritually.

Autumn: Do plenty of gentle physical exercise, such as stretching, yoga or t'ai chi. Take walks in beautiful places, and expeditions to museums and galleries. Watch comedy films.

Winter: Massage on waking, before lunch and before bed for 20 minutes; always massage away from the heart in long sweeping strokes. A high protein diet is important, so eat a balanced diet of fish and grains, but no meat of any kind. Choose red and orange fruit and vegetables; apricots are particularly good.

The nature of Phlegm humour

Phlegm, which originates in the right chest, is a quiet, deeply placed, energetic function that is concerned with holding everything together, physically and mentally. It is best visualised as a slow-moving, clear, sticky glue that binds yet encourages growth. Phlegm influences bones, muscle growth, metabolic functions and all of the body's major cycles, as well as the nature of how we create memories and what we perceive to be true or false.

Phlegm energy inspires deep thinking and an interest in philosophy, plus a desire for creativity of all sorts, from making money to works of art. In balance, Phlegm types prefer simple light foods and are happy enabling others to find fulfilment and well-being.

Phlegm can become imbalanced if any individual is very shy, overly serious, emotionally locked up or denies their own capacity for any higher sense of happiness or spirituality. As they dress themselves in a Phlegmatic overcoat to protect themselves from emotional pain, so they start to erode the body's ability to self-heal, and diminish their mental abilities.

Human society could not evolve and progress without this humour because it gives us a sense of continuity, history and cultural awareness. All religious structures are Phlegmatic, so too are institutions like banks, the stock exchange, the armed forces and the government.

Charitable organisations, such as the Salvation Army, are Phlegmatic in nature due to their desire to improve people's lives and bring stability. Negative Phlegm influences can be seen in people who allow themselves to be defined by their job, also in the obstructive red tape of big bureaucracies.

CHARACTERISTICS OF BEING IN BALANCE

The Phlegm-dominant/Wind-subdominant combination enables people who uphold tradition and want to create lasting institutions that will help others. They know instinctively how to use material forces for the benefit of society. Phlegm/Wind people tend to be chubby, introvert, brooding and of average height.

Phlegm/Bile types also respect tradition, but they have no qualms in ripping down outdated traditions and creating waves in general. They are the people who will use their mental energy to create new ways of thinking, employing the written word as their chosen means of communication.

Phlegm-dominant people often feel cold, chilly or uncomfortable in their bodies, regardless of weather and environment. They have a tendency to put on weight and have a pale complexion. They have strong constitutions that act very slowly. Normally they have a long life span. They like sour-tasting foods and drinks, and are often smokers.

Phlegm combined with Bile makes the person very sensual, with a leaning to artistic and physical expression. They are often tall, with a lithe body, and their skin has a bronze tint to it. They may suffer from a superiority complex and be easily influenced by superficial things.

SYMPTOMS OF PHLEGM IMBALANCE

Phlegm: Skin outbreaks and diseases, eye problems, lung disorders, hormonal problems, lack of virility, problems conceiving and in pregnancy, eating disorders, weight problems, bone disorders, depression that turns to violence, alcohol addiction, mental collapse, burn out from work or other circumstances.

Phlegm/Wind: As above but this combination experiences one or more symptoms very intensely over a long time because the Phlegm humour dominates the healing Wind humour, rather like a brick (Phlegm) sitting on a feather (Wind) and pinning it down.

Phlegm/Bile: As above, but the symptoms would normally become apparent only at a time of stress.

HOW TO HEAL PHLEGM IMBALANCES ACCORDING TO THE
SEASONS

Spring: Eat lots of fish and cooked vegetables, pulses and grains, with a little red meat twice a week. Avoid alcohol, coffee and tea. Take a lot of physical exercise, especially manual work and swimming, in rivers or the sea, if possible. Spend 10 minutes daily in a sauna or steam room. Massage with a strong-smelling ointment or balm for 40 minutes, three times a week in the middle of the afternoon is helpful. Cooking and baking, and simply talking to friends around a kitchen table are healing.

Summer: Aim to live in a warm, dry, gently breezy environment with lovely scenery, beautiful views and wide open spaces. Play romantic music. Stay calm in the morning and take light activity in the after-noon. Eat in the same way as for spring. Massage three times daily for 15 minutes to one hour before each meal in a strong, continuous, circular, anticlockwise movement, using chickpea flour or talc. Go to bed before 10pm to encourage the body's cycles to improve the humoural balance.

Autumn: Again, take lots of exercise and eat as in spring and summer, avoiding alcohol, coffee and tea. Massage yourself with warm oil for one hour on waking, twice a week; always massage down the body from the head to the feet in short gentle strokes. Take a hot bath for 10 minutes in the mid-afternoon every day.

Winter: Massage as above three times a week on waking. Eat fish and grains, with a little spice in the evenings only, but no meat at all. Also avoid salt, which causes further imbalance.

IMPROVING HUMOURAL BALANCE BY OVERCOMING OBSTRUCTIONS

Once again, Tibetan medicine regards illness as an obstruction that can damage the humours and make you susceptible to illness. However, obstructions of all kinds can be transformed by the use of emotional tools. Below you will find simple descriptions of how to do this in your everyday life.

These tools lead us to examine how we see the everyday material world, with all its pressures and its fragile social structure. The mainstays of our world view are ourselves, our circumstances and other people. By understanding how we think about ourselves, we can know how we create the foundations of health and illness. If our attitude is unbalanced or confused, we run the risk of creating obstructions which prevent us from experiencing mental, physical and spiritual health.

The starting place is to learn how we relate to other people, what we say and how other people react to what we say. We also need to assess what the words we choose say about us, when we are speaking in anger, for example, or in the throes of passion, love or any other emotion.

Attitudes towards our work and how we identify with it are also key to how we set up our relationship with others. Work, in this context, means any activity we undertake with which we identify strongly. For most of us, that means thousands of daily tasks, big and small.

Stress is a major obstruction these days. But people respond quite differently to the pressure: a sensible person might allow themselves to collapse and rest the moment they can, while a more foolish one would fight on and later find themselves burnt out and ill.

Prejudice, too, can create obstructions. Prejudice of any sort is the opposite to higher thinking: it represses people into states of worthlessness and triviality. Illness, according to Tibetan medicine, is a prejudice that you have created against yourself.

Transforming your view of yourself and your situation in the ways described below can help you to overcome obstruction and create well-being in your life. We all have within us the cures to our problems and illness. We are both the medicine and the healer.

Ten insights into obstructions

1. RELATIONSHIPS OF ALL TYPES

People are other people's biggest problem. Think of the numbers of people you have to deal with every day at home and work: husbands, wives, children, parents, relatives; friends and lovers; colleagues, employees and bosses; trades people, spiritual advisors or other mentors – not to mention the man in the street.

The heart of successful relationships is good communication. Everyone wonders what makes other people tick, what they're thinking about and how they can change it. But, so often, we expend huge energy trying to communicate and end up with little to show for it.

The most common type of obstruction is communicating clearly, and dealing with difficult situations or people. Remember that a difficult person is a difficult situation. This exercise will reduce the amount of problems you experience with people every day.

The ancient Tibetans discovered a simple way to heal poor communication, and to establish trust, power and spiritual abundance. It is this: sometimes you have to get tough, other times you have to be gentle, and others you need to be neutral. Of course, you have to know what to be at the appropriate time, and you can do this by developing a very simple mental skill, which quickly will become part of your everyday thinking. It goes like this.

When you are in a meeting or any other situation with other people, listen to them actively. In your mind, direct your mental energy into the words that they speak and you will find that you can see – behind their language – the truth of what they are really saying.

Once you hear the truth behind their words, you know how you should act, whether that is to be tough, neutral or gentle. This in itself enables you to prevent obstructions from occurring in the first place, or heal existing ones.

Obstacles become obstacles because they are given unskilful energy, and so become difficult to move. When you get a response of any kind from an obstacle, it starts to move. Once this happens, you can start to resolve the problem.

2. EMPLOYMENT AND RELIGION

Work, career or any activity that is involved in making a living means creating an identity for the worker. That means setting up some kind of power base, which inevitably leads to politics (with a small 'p'). Religion or any other hierarchical organisation involves the same.

The Tibetans believe that this manipulating is part of human nature; that in these sorts of situations, people come to believe that their activities and their emotions are the same. So they invest the energies of control into what they are doing and seek to stamp their personalities on it indelibly, so other people must sit up and take notice of them.

This can be a good or a bad thing. In the end, however, the closer the identification becomes, the more likely it is that work itself becomes the obstruction. Eventually, it prevents the individual from becoming balanced.

The answer is this. If you are taking a position in any organisation, do the following: know where the power comes from and who holds it, discover who holds all the emotional energy in your work community, and observe how the power holder and the emotion holder affect everyone else. Then see if you want to be part of it.

Contrary to popular belief, you can take your money with you when you die. How? Because most people are emotionally attached to their cash, and it is this emotional attachment that is, during life, actually more important than the cash. The same energy occupies the dying person's consciousness.

Of itself, money is invisible. Sure there are cash notes, coinage, cheques and credit cards, but all of these are simply ways of representing money. Money is, and has always been, an agreement of value and a symbol of trust.

The energy of money is like the wind, invisible but felt all around the world. It is an aspect of humankind's higher thought made manifest in the material world.

Money is a mirror into which few people have the courage to look, but doing so can help you to attract large amounts of cash. Remembering that money is a process of thought and energy, start by sensing the energy of money in the everyday world around you. Notice the way money influences your life, your culture and the development of your country and the global community.

Now look at how you make your living. This must be in accordance with what makes you happy. Many people make lots of money from an occupation that does not make them happy and then, like a time bomb, there comes a point when their money becomes an obstruction in itself. They lose it by one means or another – devaluation, huge tax bills or bad advice. Alternatively, making money suddenly loses its allure.

The ancient Tibetan approach to attracting and keeping your money is simple. Remember that money is energy and you need to balance it. Remember that money, cash, cards, stocks, debts and bills are merely symbols of this energy. Remember, too, that although this energy can be stern and unforgiving you have the power to change that.

Now meditate on this energy by focusing for a few minutes once a day on all your financial assets, big or small. Concentrate on them one by one and send them positive thoughts, telling them to increase and multiply so that they benefit you and others.

Remember that in today's world, your bank account, for example, is not a solitary financial island but is connected to other financial systems, so the same money energy flows throughout the world as it does through your bank account.

As you understand this connection, you will be able to send your mental energy out from your financial island. Imagine your energy as a big ship sailing world-wide, bringing back financial abundance to your island and also dropping off blessings to other islands throughout its voyage.

Always give what you can afford to others less fortunate. Money energy that is surplus should be shared, not stored. Wealth is what money can do for you in regard to other people. If this energy is abused, it seeks retribution and does not stay long with a mean master.

4. HEALTH: HOW TO CREATE IT, KEEP IT AND USE IT

Like money, health is an energy that must be balanced, looked after and used wisely. The simplest way to care for your health is to respect your body, respect your mind, and respect your speech and thoughts, as I describe in this book. You are not a commodity. You are a highly refined consciousness in a physical form. You are sacred.

5. GOOD FORTUNE: HOW TO MAKE IT, KEEP IT AND USE IT

Good fortune comes about when the energies of your body and mind click together. This is not just about the creation of wealth: good fortune is the experience when you know deep inside you that everything is right with the world. It is when you and the divine enjoy each other's company.

Good fortune is a natural state of mind that is part of who you are. It is inside you, just waiting to be released. Start by asking for it. Be humble and receive. If you seek good fortune unskilfully – in other words, selfishly – you will create obstructions.

It never comes in the way you expect it, so open your heart for a happy surprise. You keep your good fortune by sharing it and learning from it, not by showing it off. Use your good fortune by showing other people how to access it, based on your own experience.

6. REPETITIVE OBSTRUCTIONS: WHY PROBLEMS KEEP COMING BACK

Obstructions that return repeatedly do so because they have not been healed. They are also trying to tell you how to deal with the problem. The answer to an obstruction always lies in the problem itself.

Firstly, look at the history. When did the problems first start? Think back to how they occurred and focus on that moment, then you will discover the seed of the obstruction and its nature. Send it as much love as you can. This will start to transform the obstruction into a problem with the potential for change.

Obstructions can seem insurmountable but, by directing love to them, they are acknowledged and start to reveal what they are made of. In this way, they lose their intensity and weight. Then the essence of the problem is revealed.

Imagine, for instance, that someone is in constant debt, which they never manage to repay. In their minds, the obstruction set up by this situation has grown more powerful than the actual debt, and the obligation to pay it back. So they are unable to confront the original problem.

By directing love to this situation, however, the obstruction dissolves and the debtor creates inner distance and a new perspective on the problem. As this happens, the obstruction shows you how to heal it once and for all. So the debtor works out a way of repaying the debt, and understands how to avoid getting in the same situation again.

There are two families in your life: the family you are born to and the family you make; that is, your friends. Your relationship with your birth family influences how you make and value friendships. If you have problems with family or friends, you need to start to understand the way in which the problem affects you and others.

Look at how you talk to each other, the language you all use and the type of words you use to express emotions. If you use harsh words or swear words to express what you feel, you will only serve to separate the opportunities for healing. Gentle words that are firm and direct, asking a question that needs a response, are better.

People choose harsh words because they are unsure of what they really want to say. Using lots of emotionally loaded words with open-ended questions is the same. A sentence such as, 'Damn you, you never pay attention to what I say' may express how you feel, but it also places an energetic affliction on the person to whom you say it. So it is also important to listen to what people say with your heart and intelligence, not just with your reactive emotions.

As you explore this, you will become aware of the emotional forces at the heart of most communication and you can understand what people really mean. You start to see how obstructions occur and how they influence your life and the lives of your family and friends. Once this takes place, you are able to start a process of honest communication.

But changing yourself may be all that you can do. Your friends and family may not truly want to communicate from the heart. They may not even want honesty. Remember, it's up to them.

8. SPIRITUAL NEEDS

Most people go through life firmly avoiding their spiritual needs. However, it is vital to consider this area. You may find that what you need is vastly different to what you imagined. The first step is to be prepared to recognise that you do not know anything at all. This is tough! But after the mental shock of accepting this has passed, you understand that you are more than your name, your body and your reputation, your bank balance and your desires. All of these cover up your inner spiritual consciousness, and it is this internal knowledge that shows you what you truly are and what you truly know.

Often we embark on things in life that we believe are important – a job, say, a campaign or a relationship – only to discover that they did not satisfy us in the way we had thought. This is because nothing that is external to us can deliver the satisfaction that our everyday mind hopes for. We forget that all we need to find satisfaction in our lives is to connect with our inner selves and to understand that spirituality exists in everything we do.

The inner self speaks to us continously but often our everyday mind cannot recognise the words. Our inner wisdom knows that everything in the everyday world has a spiritual essence. Spiritual growth starts with the most ordinary things you do each day, from cleaning the house to brushing your teeth. And it is through these mundane activities that you will find your inner divinity, not in a job title, bank balance or relationship.

9. RIGHT ACTIONS, SKILFUL THOUGHTS

Right actions come from skilful or right thinking. Right action means doing what is right for you and for other people; it also means taking responsibility for the action you have done.

Skilful thoughts means a thinking process that enables you to be happy, focused and calm, and, in this way, support your actions. Skilful thoughts also help you to come to an understanding of your own inner morality and ethical framework, so understanding your spiritual needs is vital. This is an individual thing, differing from person to person.

The ancient Tibetans believed that, although society and religious beliefs should have basic rules and guidelines, each person must find their own morality and ethics. This is the foundation for emotional and spiritual maturity.

10. CREATING GOOD ENERGY

By focusing on these areas of your life, you will see the nature of the problems and obstructions that are common to virtually everyone on this planet. Simply starting the process of changing them will help to cultivate stronger mental energies. All you need is to be willing to try.

At times in our lives, we may come across obstructions that are so powerful, the only way to transform the situation is to accept it with humility and grace. Then you will be able to see the spiritual significance of why the problem could only be changed in this way.

At times, you can change your circumstances only by embracing the spiritual within you.

<~>

These ten areas of obstructions can be understood and overcome by using the ten ways to create well-being below. For every problem that you may encounter, these techniques will show you how to turn things around.

 # TEN WAYS TO CREATE WELL-BEING

These ten ways come from a section of Tibetan Bön teachings known as 'The Way of the Shen of the Cha'. They can be used as a form of internal divination to help you increase the quality and quantity of your happiness, improve your vitality and help you to be more successful in all your chosen activities.

Each way is accompanied by a traditional action on which to focus, which stimulates the mind and body. I have adapted some of them slightly so that they make sense to people living in a global and modern world. However, the content of each way stems from ancient Tibetan wisdom that has been refined over thousands of years.

Each Way is a channel that can direct this experience both from within you and out into the world. You can use any one of the ten ways that seems most relevant, or you can use all ten over a ten-day period. If you are attracted to a particular way, do it for 10 days at the same time each day.

These ten ways of thought and action are useful tools for creating mental and emotional awareness in how you conduct your daily life. Expect results as soon as you start.

They introduce you gently to a new reality, which is often quite different to the version you are currently occupying. They are tools for living the life you want, and for acquiring power and wisdom.

THE FIRST WAY

Treating your illness with kindness will encourage faster recovery or resolution. You will gain a stronger mental approach to life so that you can direct your actions in accordance with your aims.

The action

In your mind, imagine a seed starting to grow from the earth. Watch it turn into a beautiful tree with pink flowers and golden fruit. The flowers have a most beautiful smell and the fruit is sweet and juicy. Smell the flowers so that you become the perfume. Eat the fruit so that you become the taste. Some of the flowers and fruit fall into the earth and, as the tree dies, a new one grows exactly as before.

THE SECOND WAY

Dwell upon those aspects of your life that can be improved. As you take the action below, you will gain deep insight into the qualities of your potential.

The action

A fragile golden bell sways with the wind. It is suspended by a red and gold thread covered in little knots hung across a brass frame in the shape of a circle. You pick up a long, delicate silver hammer from a red cushion. The hammer head is in the shape of an elephant with a raised trunk. At the end is a perfectly shaped sphere covered in engraved petals of a flower. You breathe in and out slowly, then gently strike the bell. The tone of the bell is soft at first then grows like a beautiful voice within you. Your mind becomes clear.

THE THIRD WAY

If you want to overcome the energies of anger, lust and greed, you need to understand how you created them and gave them life.

The action

What anger, lust and greed want most of all is recognition. Think of them as three unruly children who mimic everything you say and do. Shouting at them to stop does nothing. Anger is dressed in black clothes, lust in red, greed in green. Acknowledge them, asking each one by name what they want to say and what they are trying to tell you. Listen carefully and with humility. You will get a reply, although it may not be to your liking at first. As they speak, give them as much love as they can receive. This will change them forever and you for the better.

THE FOURTH WAY

You are not a slave to life. Life is a mountain range through which you can navigate using your internal direction finder, which comes from developing discernment and discretion.

The action

In front of you are three bowls, one full of diamonds, the second emeralds and the third rubies. As you watch them, the bowls and their precious contents merge into one unit. In your mind's eye, start to separate them bowl by bowl, jewel by jewel, until they are as they were before.

THE FIFTH WAY

Become aware of how and where your body stores stress and negativity. By knowing this, you can stop it from happening.

The action

In your mind, you are lying on your back, stretched out and at ease. A violet light appears over your head and starts to flow down and across your body, fading as it passes over your feet. You feel warm. Slowly, patches of black and of grey appear over your body where you feel most stressed and anxious. In the areas of black, focus a gold light to release stress from your physical body. In the areas of grey, focus a pink light to release stress from your mental body.

THE SIXTH WAY

You suspect that your job is making you ill. Perhaps it brings out one side of your personality at the expense of other aspects of your life. If so, this is creating unneeded negativity that will diminish your mind and body, and your happiness.

The action

Contemplate this image. A man (this applies equally to women) works all day long to provide the best for the family. Then he starts to work at night, too. He becomes so obsessed by the emotional attachment to his work that he doesn't notice that he has grown apart from his spouse and family. Suddenly he loses his job. He has no work and no connection to his family. This man or this woman now has nothing.

This nothing is the best possession anyone could ever have. He (or she) discovers that he is not his job. We can all create employment by knowing who we are and who we have the potential to be. This is also true for our families.

This situation happens every day all over the world. It is part of human nature, but it can be changed.

THE SEVENTH WAY

Examine how your food and drink affects your mood and the way your body responds to what you eat. This will show you what foods are best for you and how your mind affects the food you have eaten.

The action

Treat everything you eat and drink with respect, whether it is health food, home-cooking, restaurant fare or junk food. What matters is not what you eat but how you eat it. Your attitude creates the effects your food has upon your body and mind and therefore your attitude to the way you live and regard other people. Eating with respect is the same as praying. Food is prayer in action. Every morsel is an exercise in consciousness.

THE EIGHTH WAY

Every time we speak, we change other people's lives. Be aware of what you say, of the thought processes behind it, and its influence upon others.

The action

Repeat this slowly, out loud, word by word:

What is the most potent weapon in the history of humankind? Forget terrorism, nuclear bombs, and napalm and biological weapons, although they are all horrific. The greatest weapon is the human tongue and the way it is used. Speech is the action of thought; it affects people's lives in subtle ways, often forever. When you insult others you insult yourself. Genuine praise or other forms of compassionate or honourable language, however, act as gifts. They can bring humility to the speaker and insight and power to the listener. Speech is one of humankind's greatest achievements because it comes from the desire to communicate truth and share common feelings. Do not let your speech be taken for granted by others or yourself. It is not a commodity but a sacred event. Often it is better to be silent than to say something foolish. Silence teaches us the value of language. May peace be upon me and upon the world.

THE NINTH WAY

Activate your inner truth and your own morality by allowing yourself to be as good as you can. Life is a series of emotional and intellectual constructions – the architecture of the mind. If you understand how your mind influences all aspects of your life, you will become less reactive to life's difficulties.

The action

Take ten minutes a day to be silent. Listen to your thoughts. Use your inner senses to see what they are made of. See what is important to your life and also what activities in your life detract from your sense of good-ness. This is not easy, but it is worthwhile. You will be surprised at how much goodness lies inside you waiting to be used. As you connect to your goodness, you become still and more focused; you are not so easily distracted by events, actions of life and other people's thoughts and desires. This starts to create a foundation for wisdom. Your wisdom is your power.

THE TENTH WAY

Give thanks for the good times and the bad. Forgive all those who have hurt you and ask for forgiveness for yourself.

The action

Imagine you have thousands of beautiful white flowers, each with a different perfume. Smell each one very slowly, putting your attention into each bloom. In front of you is a fire in a triangular hearth, painted in yellow and red triangular patterns, with the point of the triangle pointing away from you. Put your attention into the fire. Now pick up one flower at a time and think of a hurt, or a state of anger, lust, greed or hate that was sparked off by an action taken by you or someone else.

Say aloud the name of the person you are dealing with, or describe the situation, and thank them three times over, whether the experience was good or bad. This helps you to let go of the past, of pain and of the cycle of suffering. It also stops dangerous and bad situations from becoming worse.

Put the emotion of these negative experiences into a flower and then place it into the fire. Watch the flower burn. Do this with each flower until they are all gone. Say again the name of the person or description of the situation, and thank them. This will help to termi-nate the particular cycle of suffering. The past will lose its sting.

Finally, at the end of this chapter, there are three very important points to remember. Just as the ten ways are directives for action and insight, so these three simple points can be seen as mental stepping stones on your path to a balanced and wise life.

1. Illness and health come from the same inner workings of your mind. All aspects of the material world, including your thoughts, are created by how you view reality.

2. As an individual, you are made up of five threads of mental energy. Your mind fabricates these in order to make sense of the world. They are: awareness, acceptance, determination, discernment and attachment. These five threads weave themselves into all human activity.

Awareness enables you to understand how you come to suffer and what your true needs are.

Acceptance of your own circumstances and situations that you cannot change (principally other people) makes you aware of karma and brings compassion.

Determination helps you to overcome all obstacles.

Discernment helps you to find the essence and truth of all things.

Attachment is the thread around which the other four are wrapped. By knowing how you are attached to things and why, you start to become less attached and begin to know what is truly important to you in your life.

3. Regardless of your actions and thoughts, you, like everyone else, originate from the energy of fundamental goodness. Life's experiences can make you forget this, which causes pain. To be as good as you know how is the first and last medicine that will, in time, heal all things.

CHAPTER SEVEN
Recovery and Rejuvenation

Healing is all about rejuvenation. It is your right. Take it and use it for your own benefit, and for the benefit of everyone else, too. Learning the process of rejuvenation is easy because the innate ability to do so is within you at every level.

The wisdom in this chapter will help you to get the most out of your life, and to discover the essence of living. You will discover the theory of the five elements that make up everything in the universe, and how to use this knowledge in a series of self-healing exercises, how to make friends with your body, and how to achieve high energy, deep focus and lasting concentration.

Being ill is a difficult experience. As you discovered in Chapter 6, Tibetan medicine looks at the foundations of illness and the path to healing like this: people suffer and get ill, both physically and emotionally, through ignorance of the appropriate way to create well-being. If they have the right means to cure their suffering, however, illness can become health and balance.

In order to help yourself get well and stay well, you need to go to the original influence that made you ill and heal it. Then your body, mind and life will start to rejuvenate. You will feel as if you have been reborn. You will be younger in mind, spirit and body. The process of ageing will slow down and your wisdom will increase.

Getting well . . .

Firstly, let us consider the basic steps of recovery that we all go through when regaining well-being whether the illness is physical, emotional, mental or spiritual. These are:

- Recovery: The process of becoming stable when your mind and body are no longer adversely affected by sickness.
- Renewal: When your body and mind start to repair and you are no longer sick.

. . . *And staying well*

This is the step that we need to take if we want true health.

- Rejuvenation: When you discover the underlying cause of your condition through a mental or spiritual process so that both your life and your state of mind are totally transformed.

Rejuvenation is both an attitude of mind, a statement of consciousness and a physical process. It is your physical body transforming itself into a higher physical state. This is joyful and powerful. And it is forever. Even though your body will die at some point, the experience of rejuvenation will live on in your soul and the souls of others.

Rejuvenation renews your senses, body, brain, intellect and emotions. As you experience heightened vitality, mental clarity and spiritual integration, this in turn empowers your soul and brings self-knowledge.

All of us need to discover the knowledge to rejuvenate but some people are more obviously in need than others. You may perhaps have had to communicate with, or look after, someone who is very ill or in constant pain, terminally ill or seriously injured. You may sense that they seem dormant. Their breathing does not seem to give them life, to inspire them. You often notice the same thing with people who always seem to be sick with chronic complaints, such as colds, aches and pains, sore bones, or headaches.

For all these people, illness has become a routine that is essential to their life. They need their problem and have lost their true selves in it. They need to recover, renew and rejuvenate. The means to do so are contained within the theory of the five elements.

All things within this world and in the cosmos at large, including your body and mind, are in a state of intertwining flux and form. These forces seem powerful, valid and real but, in fact, they are all fleeting and impermanent, in a continuous process of change. Every aspect of thought and belief, of the physical world and of the universe, is born, has its time, dies and is recycled again into energy. The weavers of this vast tapestry are, according to Tibetan belief, the five elements – Earth, Water, Fire, Wind/Air and Space.

The influence of the five elements defines the universe and the laws of nature, including the energetic relationships of your mind and body. This means that everything in the material world, great and small, starts and finishes with the elements. They are also intrinsically connected to our health through the three humours of Wind, Bile and Phlegm, which you have discovered in the previous chapter. Knowing the five elements and how they work with the three humours can enable you to understand your place in the material world.

The nature of the five elements is hard for the Western mind to accept. They are simultaneously symbolic, descriptive, subjective and actual. Confusingly, they do not always refer literally to the physical elements after which they are named, but this need not concern you now. They are the energies that make all things work, from the universe to the solar system, from lunar influences to the world at large, from your nation to your city and community, and, of course, your body.

The five elements are crucial to health because they are the basic ingredients for the origins and the cure of disease. The qualities of each element are aspects of our consciousness. Each creates deep-seated structures that support our unconscious minds and our instinctual drives and intuition. They form the way we view ourselves and build our personalities.

When the elements are out of balance in your life, things may not work the way you want them to. By balancing the elements, you experience a spontaneous understanding about them and an awareness of the energies of the natural world. Then you begin to gain great insight into the nature of your personality, releasing huge amounts of energy that you can use to benefit yourself and others.

We can harness the potential of the five elements to help us by using meditations incorporating visualisation. These are detailed later. Don't worry, by the way, if you find it hard to picture things in your mind, just following the instructions will bring good results.

EARTH

Earth is the material nature of things: matter, weight, durability and density. It rules the structure of our body – the muscular and skeletal systems – and the way we respond to our surroundings.

This element is involved in creating all types of muscle in the body, all aspects of bone development, bone marrow and the growth of skin, eyes and their functions. It influences smell and also the way in which our physical senses interact with each other. Earth also awakens our perception of time and the experiences of daily living, death and birth.

The earth element connects us to the underlying rhythms of our health and shows us what to learn from becoming ill, and the wisdom to be gained within that. It reflects our consciousness back in our faces and shows us who we really are, reminding us of our impermanence.

Earth provides stability, direction, discipline and tolerance.

WATER

Water influences the composition of our bodies and our emotional needs. It is essentially the lubricating generative force that unites the merging of matter between the subatomic world and the cellular one. In our bodies, it is the cohesive factor driving all the major systems.

This element is involved in creating all aspects of body fluids, from urine, lymph and blood to all types of discharges and fluids, both internal and external. Water directs taste and its process within the body. It influences how we become ill and the effects of that illness, as well as giving us energy to prevent us from becoming ill. This element influences religious thought, emotions, changes in human history and the development of faith.

Water creates fluid thought, compassion, intuitive and empathetic qualities, humility and generosity.

FIRE

Fire influences and directs the health of our body and mind. It is the evolution and growth of matter; within the body it is heat, digestive functions and the spark within the regulatory systems of the metabolism.

The Fire element helps strengthen the immune system, our body's defence against illness. It controls body temperature, influences circulation and heart function, and also our sight. Fire can show us why we get ill and how all things in the body become disconnected when one part is sick. It influences the worlds of money, business and career.

Fire creates the desire for overcoming obstructions, self-development, inspiration, wisdom and joy.

WIND/AIR

Wind/Air is the powerful moving force that influences oxygenation and circulatory, pulmonary, neural and lymphatic movement. It sparks cardiac function, influencing heart chambers to pump, while it regulates brain function, creating the invisible link between mind, personality and body function. Wind/Air creates the way in which we react to other people.

Wind/Air controls and directs breathing and all metabolic aspects of respiration. It governs the functions of the body's organs. Because it influences touch, Wind/Air helps you – unconsciously – to have a knowledge of your immediate environment. It also influences academic thought and discipline.

Wind/Air creates and enquiring mind, love of knowledge and reasoning, respect for community and the desire for freedom.

SPACE

Space is the underlying element that forms the development of our physical and mental personality. It allows the dynamic interplay of the other elements. This element creates all spaces, orifices and cavities in every part of your physical body and your mind; it is our potential for expanded awareness. It also influences the ability to think creatively.

This element influences your hearing and everything associated with it; for example, hearing good news or bad, and listening to gossip. Space is the potential for consciousness to be evolved and liberated; it reveals the highest in all human nature.

Exploring the concept of elemental space can reveal to us how and why we make ourselves sick, and also help us to activate rejuvenation.

HOW TO UNDERSTAND AND USE YOUR ELEMENTAL NATURE

At the start or end of each season, you can start to gain insight in your elemental nature simply by watching as the seasons change. You can also tune into the moon when it is either full or new, looking at it and allowing your senses to feel it. As you do this, focus on the elements one by one. You will sense them within you. Start to feel which one is more dominant and which are weak.

As you look at the natural world, note the correspondences between the elements. Then examine your personality and see how it relates to the elements in nature that attract you the most.

Make an elemental circle by drawing a circle on a large piece of paper and writing in the names of the five elements. Use a different colour for each – choose ones that you think match them. Then write in your feelings about each element. You will slowly begin to build up a personal elemental circle and be able to see which is balanced and which not.

The more you do this simple exercise, the more you will start to stimulate deeply conscious pathways between your everyday mind and the elements. Creating this elemental circle will also start to show you which of your habits are fuelled by a particular element and help you to gain insight into how to improve things.

Elemental imbalances

These are caused by emotional negativity. If we cannot understand that we are the cause of our suffering and blame our problems on external events, the negativity will increase, activating the elemental imbalances even more.

If we become used to perceiving only suffering or bad experiences, we create mental pain for ourselves. When we focus unskilfully upon the cause of our unhappiness – or endlessly question our right to happiness – the experience intensifies until it is bound to collapse, causing us further unhappiness and disrupting our elemental harmony. Then, whatever we experience – good or bad – we treat with suspicion. That's a great shame because it means we lose connection with our inherent openness and innocence.

Using the five elements to activate rejuvenation

Genuine lasting change can only happen if you transmute the patterns in your life that cause you illness or recurring pain. This means becoming a more balanced person than you were before you were sick. You need to identify how your body stores pain, reacts to it and then expresses it.

We can use the five elements to help us. Each of them is a key to knowing about the story of your body. Crucially, in order to change, you need to feel that within you there is the space or emotional room for this to happen.

If you are finding it hard to bend your mind to instigate the first steps of rejuvenation, the problem is that the Phlegm humour is restricting the possibilities of growth and change. The self-healing exercise below will help to transform your thought patterns and heal blocked emotions. It combines the skilful use of Fire (motivation), Wind/Air (movement) and Space (the possibility of change).

SELF-HEALING EXERCISE 1

This will help to heal blocked emotions and stimulate change.

Sit or lie down comfortably. Focus on your breathing.

With your mind and breath, start to try and feel all the cavities in your body. Take your time. Feel the shapes of the cavities and orifices of your body, including your mouth, sinuses, bladder, stomach, intestines and ears. You can also explore the cavities in your joints, nostrils, eye sockets, etc.

Use your breath to gain a sense of the size and depth of these cavities. Once you can do this, let your mind fill those spaces. Then imagine all of them merging into one.

Feel the element of Wind/Air flowing through this larger space, all through your body, into your bones. Moving, clearing and cleaning any and all types of obstructions, both physical and mental.

Your desire for change starts to unfold as a feeling of physical strength. Your body becomes relaxed and feels stretched out.

At this point, you feel your bodily cavities start to generate heat.

Slowly, a gentle fire begins to emanate from the spaces, warming your whole body, flowing through your bloodstream, relaxing your skeleton and strengthening your desire to be free from illness.

Let your body rest in this warmth and start to see yourself becoming well and going about your life filled with power, joy and strength.

Do this exercise slowly, twice a day if you can, at home and at work, for thirteen days in a row. It will give you courage and help you to feel in control again, but in a new way. You will feel at home in your body.

<~>

Rachel had long term Chronic Fatigue Syndrome and regular attacks of severe asthma. Most of the time she was in bed, angry and ill. She felt completely power-less and trapped by her condition. She got to the stage of giving up trying to get well. So she got worse.

Then she decided to try Tibetan medicine. After a few months she felt a little better and was introduced to this self-healing exercise, which she used as part of her treatment. Her attitude became much more posi-tive and within a year she was up and about. After another year, her asthma disappeared completely. She is now able to work, as a result of her combined package of treatment.

The exercise empowered Rachel to understand the nature of her physical suffering. 'I felt powerless, out of control and didn't know what to do. I gained a huge amount by using the meditation exercise, and became more connected. I am able to direct my own life now, instead of leaving it to doctors, parents or friends. At last, I am truly independent.'

<~>

Rejuvenation and recovery are not the same

'Recovery is a valley, rejuvenation is a mountain', according to an old Tibetan saying. This means that you can get better without knowing why you were sick, which means that you can become ill again. Rejuvenation is the total renewal of mind and body so that from the mountain peak you have a complete view of the valley below and can detect all the complexities of the landscape.

Sickness is not greater than you; it is part of you, defined by your experience of living. To have the full picture of your sickness means you can decide to have power over whatever ails or influences you, and can determine the outcome.

It is important to understand that your inner mind goes through the rejuvenation experience first. Then, like a flash of bright light, it floods the physical body with energising and healing power. All of this is latent within you, a submerged frequency of energy waiting to be used.

The process is called a *jinlab* or 'wave of grace' in Tibetan, a moment of spiritual beauty that is both ascending and descending. You can receive this blessing from others, but you can also give it to yourself.

<~>

Charles had Motor Neurone Disease. He knew he was near death and was terrified of dying painfully by suffocation. He came to believe that nothing could change his illness, that in some way he was being 'punished' for whatever bad things he had done in the past. As his body let him down, he felt more powerless by the day.

Charles had been famous all over the world for half a century, but he knew his fame could do nothing to help him. At this nadir, he was introduced to the notion of rejuvenation instead of recovery.

At first he didn't see the point of doing the self-healing exercise, but finally he understood that it could help his fear of dying. In fact, it rejuvenated his inner life and, when he died a few weeks later, he had no fear.

'Overcoming my fear of death showed me not to be afraid of life,' he told me, moments before he died. 'I know why I got sick. Now I am rejuvenated. I am ready.'

At the funeral, his wife sang 'Amazing Grace'.

<~>

SELF-HEALING EXERCISE 2

This will help heal the fear of dying, both for the person and carers, friends and family. It also calms those who are frightened of success.

Focus on your heartbeat. Let its rhythms pulse through you until all you sense and feel is the heartbeat. Feel the element of Fire start to grow from a little flame, larger and larger. The beat of your heart fans the fire of rejuvenation.

Now imagine that your skin begins to glow a light red. Your body is full of this gentle fire. You start to sense the movement and heat of powerful healing energies, as the Bile humour becomes active.

As this happens, the Earth element starts to be felt in your skeleton, emerging as a powerful but gentle sensation spreading through your bones and joints, inflating your skeleton with a strong stable force.

Rest in this energy. Close your eyes and merge into it.

New body, new intelligence

The body has its own innate ability to sense the environment around it, and that unconsciously feeds into the way your mind deals with the world. By activating the Wind/Air element and the Wind humour, as in self-healing exercise 3, you can start to develop a connection with your body that gives you greater awareness of it, and more heightened senses. This establishes within you a truer sense of your physical reality and is a crucial part of the rejuvenation experience.

> *Malcolm suffered from a muscle-wasting disease, which conventional medicine was treating with a rigorous programme of drugs and exercise. When he came to see me he was unhappy and isolated. He felt his body was an enemy, a slave master to which he was manacled. Since his teens, he had wanted to be a professional tennis player, but his illness developed at much the same time and he had to give up his dream. Years of resentment against his body built up within him. Malcolm and his body did not have a good relationship. As he practised this exercise, he began slowly to transform his anger and frustration, and he started to find new ways of appreciating his body, even enjoying it. Eventually he was able to create a marvellous state of self-love within. As a result of this dynamic and healthy mind-body relationship, he exudes charisma and compassion. 'I don't hate myself any more,' he told me once. 'I feel like other people — normal.'*

<~>

This will help you to enhance your connection with your body. Focus on your breathing. With your mind, tell the Wind/Air element to circulate throughout your body; it will automatically find its own course. Now focus on the Wind humour as it moves from the top of your head down into your pelvis. The more you do this exercise, the more you will be able to feel both the Wind/Air element and the Wind humour as they travel through you.

They automatically stimulate the Earth element and your body starts to inflate with power. At the same time, the Air element helps your body to feel calm and flowing.

Relax. Be as still as you can. Let the energy of the elements and the humours activate your body to expand and stretch. As you start to feel all the physical functions of the body becoming energised and flexible, your mind merges into your body and they are one.

Be still.

Illness is communication

Becoming ill is the desperate stage in communication at which body and mind announce war on you. Emotional and physical processes under stress strive to be expressed in a form that makes you sit up and take notice. The body and the soul use a language of immediate experiences that remind us of our mortality and our fragility. And it can take place at any time, anywhere.

> *Despite being a leading academic, Harry never paid attention to his body. After many decades of this neglect, he ended up with illnesses ranging from liver and kidney disease to late onset diabetes. He was*

overwhelmed and could make no sense of what was happening to him. He felt that he had 'no space inside his head or his body'.

Harry decided to escape. He gave up his prestigious job at a famous American university and came to live in London, England. But he soon discovered that his problems travelled with him.

Nothing improved significantly until he learned to use the self-healing exercise below to break free of his confusion and allow him to listen to his body. Then he heard the clear words of health underneath the troubled buzz of sickness. He returned to America and went through a course of treatment.

Eventually he learnt how to manage both his body and his mind. Harry went back to work, and he became happy.

<~>

SELF-HEALING EXERCISE 4

This will help you to confront your fears.

Lie straight, if possible, or sit comfortably with your hands resting in your lap. Close your eyes.

Focus on your skeleton. Feel it. Imagine the Water element flowing through each bone, a pipe of life. Let your mind flow with the water in your bones. Feel its power. Let your mind allow the Water element to focus your attention.

Follow the flow until you come to rest naturally.

There is no room for habits that restrict rejuvenation

Negative patterns of behaviour, such as chain-smoking, taking drugs, or obsessional attitudes, can restrict your physical well-being and sow the seeds of illness. By knowing what is good for you and what is not, you can implement rejuvenation.

<~>

Michael, a musician, got into the habit of being sick as a means of coping with stress, fatigue and fame. He did everything he could to sabotage his own understanding of why he was ill. When he learned this self-healing exercise, he began to admit to himself that he had to give up the habits that supported his illnesses.

Step by step, this inner awareness evolved into Michael's knowing what was good for him. He started to discover a yearning for spirituality and to feel a desire for happiness. He let go of his addiction to his career and the fame that came with it, and was then able to take charge. His music improved and so did his record sales. So did his happiness. He no longer isolates himself, but takes a full part in his local community.

<~>

SELF-HEALING EXERCISE 5

This will help to heal addiction of any type and enhance the ability to see through self-created illusions.

Lie on your back. Focus on your belly, the source of physical power. Follow the rise and fall of your breathing.

In the depth of your gut, try and feel your Water element moving through the tissues of your muscles and skin. Feel the coolness of this Water running over your skin.

Now activate your Wind humour: simply think of it and feel it spiralling up out from your groin, fanning out to the top of your head and taking with it the negativity and physical poisons. As this happens, imagine it becoming an orange light which removes and destroys all the pollution of mind and body.

Rest quietly for a few moments, just feeling the state of your body with your mind.

Your intelligent body

Whatever you think, do or experience profoundly influences your body, as does every aspect of your physical world. It absorbs all experiences and places them within your nervous system, which then creates your immediate reality.

Your mind, however, can be tricked by sensory influences, language and belief systems. It believes what it receives. But the body believes only what it can use. It stores pain, for instance, as part of its learning process.

The problem is that your body often doesn't have the means to distinguish what to keep and what to let go. Helping it to do so is a vital key to rejuvenation. You can then determine the way in which your body deals with illness and help it to create well-being.

<~>

> Matthew was always tired and in pain, with little energy for anything. His body seemed out of control and separate from his mind — he felt he was losing connection with it.
>
> Little experiences in his daily life escalated into

major dramas so that by the time he went to bed, he was so tired he could not sleep. His body had become confused by what was happening in the world around it.

He was prescribed Tibetan herbal medicine and a programme of Kum Nye exercises. When he learned the self-healing exercise below, he began to understand that he was suffering from an acute stress disorder. The exercise allowed him to discover a way of creating emotional boundaries through which he could interpret the world safely.

Based on what he learned, Matthew changed his lifestyle and was able to cure himself completely.

<~>

SELF-HEALING EXERCISE 6

This will help you to unlock your own healing abilities.

Lie down on your back or sit comfortably, hands in lap, eyes closed.

Sense your skeleton, feeling the large bones in your legs and the long bones in your arms. Feel the length of your spine and the top and back of your head. Place your sensations of these areas into your general awareness by breathing through them and letting go of any tensions.

Feel the natural connection between these areas as the energy you release seeks to move through your body. Now direct the energy back into your spine, moving from the top of your neck down through each vertebrae to the very base of your spine.

Rest and focus on your physical heart. Receive what your heart tells you. That might be feelings or emotions, physical sensations such as pain, memories, happiness, even a recipe for fish pie. Anything. Just receive.

Repair, restore, rejuvenate: you can do it!

Your body wants to grow, renew, expand, rejuvenate and survive, but it is always timid about the healing process. It needs to be encouraged like a shy child.

Cultivating positive thought is a vital part of how the body learns to stay well. You can use the fact that the body forgets nothing. Once a thought is properly placed, the body keeps it to continue to a higher state of survival.

SELF-HEALING EXERCISE 7

This will help you to have the courage to accept those things you cannot change

Lie down on your back or sit comfortably, hands in lap, eyes closed.

Now think of the Water element flowing through your body.

As you do so, focus on how your body responds when you become sick, and on whether you really view your life in a positive way. You will find that you start to remember how your body responds when you are ill.

Send the Water element like a flowing stream through your skeleton, washing away all impurities. Then do the same for all your muscles, organs and your skin. Think of sparkling drops of silver rain falling on and through you, warm and electric, renewing you from the inside out. As this silver rain falls on to you, start to breathe it in.

Feel the vitality surging throughout your body.

Loving energy is in everything

Whatever your circumstances, your immediate surroundings contain boundless positive energy.

According to Tibetan medicine, matter is slow-moving energy, and your consciousness can make any matter relax, open and become pliable. You can make it speed up or slow down. The energy in your surroundings is like a golden cup covered with grime, which your mind can clean so that it shines with love and positivity.

SELF-HEALING EXERCISE 8

To help you experience love in all things.

Lie down on your back or sit comfortably, hands in lap, eyes closed.

Focus on your breathing. As you breathe in and out slowly and deeply, focus upon the five elements – Space, Wind/Air, Fire, Water and Earth – around you. Feel each growing in powerful healing energy with every breath you take.

As you do so, the energy of the elements in your surroundings will start to be drawn towards you. As you feel this happening, focus on your physical heart and see a deep emerald green light shining there. The Five Elements flow into this light and filter into your body for immediate healing and use.

Rest and receive the energy. When you feel you cannot absorb any more, start to direct it out to all of your friends and enemies, to negative and positive situations and events, and so on out to all living creatures so that they may benefit as you have.

Using your body's inner cycle

The Tibetans believe that the material world, the universe and the mind go through cycles of rejuvenation. By working with the cycles, you unlock within yourself the basis of rejuvenation. You can use your body's inner cycle by this self-healing exercise.

SELF-HEALING EXERCISE 9

To help you understand the cycles of life and know that there is an appropriate time for all things to happen.

Stretch out on your back, with both arms and legs slightly apart. Become aware of your breathing, then your heartbeat.

Let your Wind/Air and Water elements become active. Just think about each one and in your mind say its name. Close your eyes to help you to concentrate. As you do so, you will discover — underneath the movement of your breathing and your heartbeat — other physical cycles and functions in your body.

Follow each one and you will feel them working in harmony with the next, like an orchestra. Timing, rhythm and balance are the health gifts of the body's inner cycles.

<~>

REJUVENATION IS A PATTERN

Throughout the natural world there are patterns that reveal the flux and flow of life force. Look at the patterns birds make when they fly in formation, the trails of clouds, the shapes that rivers carve through the landscape as they flow to the sea. Examine the minute detail of flowers and their petals, of sea shells, of the five-pointed star at the core of an apple sliced sideways. Once you start looking at these, you will also see the intrinsic patterns of birth, death and rejuvenation.

We human beings are as much a part of nature as flowers, sea creatures and apples, as the clouds, rivers and birds. Exactly the same patterns exist within our bodies and our lives. Your body is the universe and the natural world in miniature. Think of the constant death and renewal of skin cells every three or four weeks, of bone every two years. As they course around your body, blood cells form a pattern very like flocks

*of migrating birds and the sound of blood in your heart
is exactly like waves on the seashore.*

*You can connect with the patterns of the natural
world and feel the energy of life as the ancient Tibetans
did, using a practice they called sky-gazing. Simply
gaze up into the heavens — blue, grey, thundery, day or
night — and let your mind soar up into the expanse.
Feel its immensity. Free float around the universe.
Connect with the natural world.*

<~>

Don't judge your body, make friends with it

We all tend to judge ourselves by the way we look, how fit we are, and
how much our body can or can't do. Nourishing a positive body image
is crucial in the larger picture of well-being, but even that may slow
down the rejuvenation process.

Whether you are vain about your body or disgusted with it, the
experience comes to the same thing — obsession. The best image you
can cultivate about your body comes through listening to it and taking
care of it. Your body's true value is far greater than any human being
could ever conceive.

SELF-HEALING EXERCISE 10

This helps to show you just how precious your life is.

Lie down on your back or sit comfortably, hands in lap, eyes
closed. Breathe gently and think about the marvel that is your
body.

Let your mind remember for at least 20 minutes the experiences
gained from doing the other exercises. Now focus again on your body

and you will discover a shift in your consciousness as the rejuvenation process comes alive.

Rest.

Rejuvenation is a blessing from within

The greatest blessings that you can ever receive are those that come from yourself. This doesn't mean that they are not triggered by some external means: very often something you hear or see – a smile, music, a glint of sunshine, a line of poetry – leads to a moment of expanding consciousness within you.

Learn to be receptive to this endless river of healing, where you and the structures of the universe are intertwined in a fusion of consciousness. This is the nature of life, ever expanding and delighting in itself. Rejuvenation is a seed of energy that exists in the heart of even the most intense form of disease. You are it.

HIGH ENERGY, DEEP FOCUS, LASTING CONCENTRATION

High levels of mental and physical energy that enable you to focus deeply and with lasting concentration are a hugely desirable aspect of rejuvenation, but they can seem like an impossible goal.

The ancient Tibetans regarded three qualities of energy, each influencing a different humour, as essential tools for self-knowledge and learning how to make the most of the world.

- High energy regulates and activates the Wind humour; it is a self-sustaining mental force that creates a well of inner energy to work effectively in the everyday world.

- Deep focus stimulates and balances Bile; it is creative energy that can be used to direct the outcome of the tasks you carry out.
- Lasting concentration regulates and integrates Phlegm; it brings you insight into how you live and your personal affairs.

These three inner qualities can radically change your life for the better. By developing them through daily practice you will enable your personality to become more active and clear thinking. These powerful forces are available within you. All you need do is ask yourself whether you want them, or not. If you do, read on. There is a meditation exercise below that will enable you to rediscover these essential qualities.

You may believe that you have never had any essential qualities that define who you really are. Everyone has. You have simply forgotten them or covered them up through life experiences. They can be awakened by transmuting your spiritual and emotional potential. Then you can use them in the everyday world.

These qualities may seem more worldly than spiritual. But, as with everything in the physical world, they integrate all aspects of living – mental, physical, emotional and spiritual. Let us look at them in more detail.

HIGH ENERGY

High energy will help you to work through problems, issues or situations that seem insurmountable. This energy is everywhere, it is the building blocks of the molecular world, and the foundation of light. It can be found in your physical heart and is perfectly active within you, only seeking a harmonious connection with the material world where it can operate powerfully enough to overcome any and every type of obstruction.

Activating high energy will help you to be whole and strong, regardless of how you see yourself or your current circumstances. High

Energy develops within you compassion and the ability to stop yourself from repeating past mistakes, and to make your ideas become reality.

You will also be presented with many opportunities to create abundance and fame. This means you may have power or major influence over other people's lives. High energy enables you to be unattached to such things, while still using them skilfully. Developing this quality comes through a process of knowing why you are in the world, and identifying your true role in living. You can also develop enduring joy which is a quality of inner spiritual happiness that stays strong whatever your circumstances.

DEEP FOCUS

Deep focus comes from developing high energy. However, you need to know how to recognise, develop and treasure it. Deep focus enables you to perceive the essence of anything and so to understand it. Understanding is power and this kind of power helps you to become a better person. Being focused in this way encourages the ability to ask good questions on any subject, and to cultivate the ability to discover the truth of anything quickly. This type of focus brings a deep appreciation of the spiritual in the commonplace.

Your mind will develop greater mental clarity and be able to remember large amounts of information. It will become disciplined, giving you the ability to think clearly. Deep focus also creates a respect for money and the ability to make, keep and use it.

LASTING CONCENTRATION

As your mind becomes more connected to your body and the world, lasting concentration rises like the morning sun, spreading its light and warmth. You begin to have a physical sensation of warmth and light.

This quality will empower you to gain mental and emotional discipline so that you can finish things you start. It will also help you to bring together all types of activities, ideas and experiences so that you can make sense of your world. The qualities of this form of concentration develop patience, faith, happiness and enjoyment of the simple things in life. You are also more able to attract property, love and general good fortune.

THE DOWNSIDES OF THE ESSENTIAL QUALITIES

As well as their beneficial aspects, each of the three qualities also has negative sides, which may cause damage at a later date. The qualities only become negative if people use them unskilfully.

- The negative qualities of high energy are: extreme vanity, self-obsession, paranoia, fear of flying or being enclosed in small spaces, addictions and addictive behaviour.
- The negative qualities of deep focus are: total exclusion of other people in the achievement of your own aims; ruthless use of people or resources; anger over small things; the need to control; hoarding of resources; lack of generosity; violence towards others.
- The negative qualities of lasting concentration are: concern with detail to the exclusion of outcomes; meanness of spirit; rude behaviour for no reason; jealousy; enjoyment in other's suffering; a feeling of isolation from other people; inability to accept new ideas; a feeling that only bad things will happen or that there is no future happiness.

The ten connections

Before we go on to the meditation exercises, you will need to understand the mental connections necessary to activate and maintain the potential of these qualities. These concepts encourage your mind to accept the changes brought about by the meditation exercises and integrate them into your personality. They will help you make sense of what you discover from the meditation exercises.

1. Accept what you feel within yourself as you first start the meditation. Do not be afraid at the speed or intensity of the feelings that may emerge from this safe exercise.

2. Do not pay special attention to any images that come up in your mind or to any physical sensations that you feel from doing the meditation. These are responses from your body and mind to influences from the meditation.

3. Do not rush the exercises. Your mind and body will set their own pace. Your body can only respond at the speed it feels safe. It is conditioned by your past mental attitudes and you cannot force it to respond immediately to inner change.

4. Mental and physical energy move at different rates. Your mind moves faster than your body because it is responding to millions of types of stimulus all at once. Any changes that take place in the way your mind works will take a while to filter into your body. The meditation exercise will help to bring these two energies to a point where they will meet. You will feel the pace that they set intuitively. Do not try and force change, let it become a part of you naturally. If you can just sit back and let it come to you, you will benefit in a more complete way.

5. You will only make as much progress as appropriate. Be patient and you will help yourself. Your mental energies will find their own balance naturally.

6. As you develop these qualities, they will bring out your mental abilities in a way that will surprise you. You may find latent resources that you never knew you had. Sometimes abilities about which you were insecure suddenly revive, and your former lack of confidence fades.

7. You will find a growing connection between body and mind, unique to you. At first it will feel vague but in time it will become more definite. The more you practise these meditations, the more sensitive to each of the three qualities you will be. So that within yourself, you will know intuitively how they are affecting you.

8. Your mind will start to feel expanded and your body more relaxed. You will feel more alert and better able to carry out more complicated mental tasks. These qualities will create a better mental state and you will find that you will become more aware of how your mind works.

9. Your emotional energy will be calm. This means that the normal stresses of your everyday life will not affect you so intensely. You will know how to avoid creating further stress. This calmness will then grow and spread out into other aspects of your personality.

10. You will find that you have a more positive view about being alive. Courage, strength, fortitude and direct behaviour will be aspects of this emerging positive energy.

Meditation exercise to activate the essential qualities of high energy, deep focus and lasting concentration

Sit or lie down comfortably, eyes closed. Focus upon your physical heart. Listen to its beating. Listen to its pulse. Allow this rhythm to flow through you.

Identify with the heartbeat. As you do so, think of the heartbeat becoming a milky white light that flows over and through you. As you become infused with this light, all your fears and obstructions dissolve. The light becomes intense and more brilliant; it starts to make a flute-like sound. This washes over and through you until your persona and the workings of your mind become the same as the light and the sound.

As this happens, everything merges into an immense clear and brilliant light, silent and full of boundless perfection and beauty.

You become one with this light.

You become clear light.

<~>

As you practise this exercise in harmonious knowledge, you will discover that your mind and body become flooded with energy, happiness and serenity. When you unlock the great inner beauty, you wonder which lies at the bedrock of your consciousness. You discover your humanity and the boundless compassion that flows through you. We can offer this to each other and to all living creatures.

<~>

Compassion is a tree, rejuvenation the fruit that grows upon it.

High energy, deep focus and lasting concentration are the seeds of that fruit.

This tree never dies or withers, but is merely overgrown by brambles of the mind.

<~>

George was a retired professor of biology whose work was concerned with the very earliest cellular aspects of life. He had travelled the world in search of the meaning of life. Yet, he never felt satisfied. He became very successful, wrote books that sold well, went through three marriages and four children, and still George wondered what his life was all about.

George had felt tired for most of his life. His mind was razor sharp, but his emotions were blunt and his soul worn out. He felt separate from people around him and, more importantly, that he could not trust anyone. So he isolated himself and expected the worst from people and from life, and the worst possible circumstances for himself.

Through Tibetan medicine, he learnt that his negative way of viewing the world had become his belief system and that it was only a matter of time before all his worst case scenarios became worse case actualities. A string of bad fortune had plagued George for over two years and he was at a loss to explain it. He moaned that he had done everything in his power to improve his situation, but nothing had changed. Indeed he had done everything he knew. But he had not looked within himself. He could not use his own inner energies because he didn't know how.

When he discovered how to activate his own inner high energy by this meditation, he was first surprised then shocked at the outcome. For the first time, he discovered that his mind was more than intellect; it was a living active experience connecting him to boundless energy and a happiness that was not dependent upon this world.

His run of bad fortune lost its sting and he realised that his belief in its power had kept him feeling down-hearted and unhappy. As his fortune changed, he created positive energy, which made him feel able to make a better life for himself. He understood that he had more choices in his life, and the business of living became a sacred experience. So George cured himself of the negative emotions and thoughts that were making his life a toxic experience. He does the meditation on a daily basis.

<~>

Elizabeth was a singer who lost her voice and didn't know where to find it. One day her voice was normal. She sang successfully, without any problems. When she woke up the next day, her voice just wasn't there. She had a concert to do the following evening with all the tickets sold.

Without her voice Elizabeth felt as if she were nothing. She felt abandoned by a talent upon which she based her identity, career and reputation. She was plunged into a dark hole, from which she felt she had no way out; she felt that no one would understand. She was overcome by such fear that she could hardly move.

Her manager dragged her to see me. The first thing she did after I took her through the meditation exercise was to cry, squeak and bellow like a pig who has just realised that the farmer has invited it for lunch — and it is the lunch. After this dramatic explosion of sound and emotion, her voice slowly creaked back into life. She did her concert, and now as she tours the world she does this exercise every time before she sings.

Elizabeth learned that her voice fled because she denied her own spirituality. She had to give it a voice. When she discovered the essential qualities, she felt in her own words 'connected to the divine'.

<~>

Using these techniques allows each of us to connect with the divine in our own way. Through that connection we find the essence of living. Our mind, body and spirit are refreshed and rejuvenated.

CHAPTER EIGHT
Food and Diet

W e live in a society that is hugely anxious about diet. We worry about all manner of things: whether or not to take supplements, eat fats, choose organic produce, and avoid e-numbers. On and on goes the litany, a shopping list of uncertainty and confusion.

The last seventy years have brought a revolution in how food is grown, processed and distributed in the West. Much of it is stuffed with added compounds, from colourings and preservatives to growth hormones and antibiotics. Supermarkets dominate the world's food-buying habits, and many consumers have become used to paying the lowest possible price. We have a wide variety of foodstuffs to choose from but what of the quality and health-giving value of the produce? Does the food we choose give us vitality?

Tibetan medicine looks at it like this. Every foodstuff on the planet, in either raw or processed form, leaves its effects in the body long after it has left your body. Foods alter, transform and decide how the body works. Whatever you eat or drink becomes a psychosomatic process. The entire origin and history of the foodstuff or beverage that you have ingested is now part of your consciousness and physical body. So the food that you eat, how you feel about it, and how you behave when you prepare and eat it directly affects your state of health. The principles of Tibetan medicine can help you to use the nutrients and energies in your food to make both your body and mind happy, and cultivate well-being.

In the modern world, particularly in the West, the range now far exceeds the foods available in pre-Communist Tibet. The foods mentioned in this chapter go beyond the confines of traditional Tibetan dietary teaching, but the rules apply in the same way.

Tibetan dietary therapy is often the first medical therapy to be used, depending on the personality of the patient, their medical condition and their circumstances. In a suitable patient, the aim of dietary therapy is to increase vitality through a balanced diet. Modification of diet, if correctly diagnosed, will itself modify unskilful behaviour in the patient. Dietary changes can not only prevent internal disease from developing but help to overcome most of the symptoms affecting the ill person.

Equally, food can cause illness. Insufficient, unnecessary or unsuitable dietary choices will create disease. This comes about through a range of factors, such as not eating enough of the right food and drink for the patient's humoural type, undereating, going on crash diets, or eating too much food continuously or in a single sitting.

The Tibetans teach that it is crucial to know when to eat and when not to eat, how much to eat, and also never to overeat. It sounds simple but many people the world over have no real idea about implementing this concept.

Your body should not be overloaded with excess food. A healthy way of eating is to make sure that your stomach is filled to three-quarters of its capacity. Half of this capacity should be filled by nutritious food, and a quarter filled by liquids. This will improve your physical and mental clarity.

Happy eating

Remember, it's not just what you eat but how you eat it. The focus and care that you give your food returns to you. Health foods and fresh juices mindlessly devoured will give less benefit to your body than a lovingly made and consumed hamburger and fries, especially with a large thick milk shake you have whizzed up yourself.

Additionally, your own emotional states, habits and eating patterns can change food to become bad for you. You could end up eating your own anger, unhappiness, fear and loneliness. Never be angry when you are just about to eat because you will also poison others with your mood. Go and be angry somewhere else then come back and eat. When you are eating, your mind should be filled with clarity and peace.

Natural is best
According to Tibetan dietary wisdom, food takes on the energy of the way in which it is processed or stored. This energy – positive or negative – is then passed on to the consumer. The more naturally the food is processed, the more complete the health benefits it will give.

The eating of food connects all the individuals who made it possible for you to eat. In a perfect situation, the fewer the people in the food chain, from grower to table, the better it is for health and happiness. And that is a big argument for choosing organic, locally grown food whenever possible.

Seasonal eating
The best health comes about by eating in harmony with the seasons. But seasonal eating has largely faded thanks to supermarkets being able to supply consumer demand for all foodstuffs throughout the year. Even if you don't go the whole way, you can still integrate some seasonal eating to benefit your body, mind and spirit.

We can all picture the foods we associate with winter, spring, summer and autumn. Simply choose the vegetables, fruits, nuts, seeds, dairy products, meat and fish that appeal to you, and which typify each season.

Raw food
Tibetan medicine teaches that raw foods can carry unseen organisms that can poison the body or, if not actually poison it, cause severe changes to the digestive tract and the three humours if eaten regularly.

So raw foods, such as salads or raw meat or vegetable products, are not part of the Tibetan dietary concept, unless particular herbs are used to make them more compatible.

Cooked or partially cooked foods, however, encourage humoural balance and digestive warmth. Refrigerated food represses these qualities and confuses the energies of the food so it's better to let food warm to room temperature if you can, rather than eating it straight from the fridge.

THE SEVEN BODILY CONSTITUENTS

At the heart of Tibetan dietary therapy are the seven bodily constituents. The theory is very complex, so I have simplified it for you to understand the basic concepts. This will enable you to think about your body and mind in a new way.

The bodily constituents are the active processes in the body that give rise to health or imbalances. They are:

1. *Dangs-ma*: crucial nutrients from ingested food.

2. *Khrag*: blood made from the essential forces of *Dangs-Ma*

3. *Sha*: muscle tissues built by the primary qualities of blood.

4. *Tshil*: a particular type of fat tissue in the creation of muscles.

5. *Rus*: the many different types of body fats which create bone structure and control bone growth.

6. *rKang*: the types of marrow made from the formative structure of bones.

7. *Khu-ba*: rejuvenating fluids, both reproductive and systemic, created by pith of bodily marrow.

According to Tibetan medicine, the seven bodily constituents are an alchemic blueprint from which physical, spiritual and psychological health comes. They are the messengers of heath and disease, they control and influence ageing, and they are the means to radiant health, good skin and a balanced mind.

The seven bodily constituents are created by powerful unconscious forces that come from both our brain and body in a cycle of continual renewal from conception to death. Equally, they hold wisdom within them that is released into our conscious mind and body. So our beings are made up of this constant ever-changing cycle of the seven bodily constituents.

The Tibetan medical system views the metabolism within the processes of the seven bodily constituents. Each constituent gives a special rebirth to the nutrients as they go through this sevenfold cycle of physical transformation. All of the major organs and body systems are directly connected to this process and refine each stage of the cycle. Each cycle results in by-products and waste products, which are then eliminated.

When a cycle becomes dysfunctional, there is potential for illness. From a Tibetan medical viewpoint, many illnesses can be found in the dysfunctions or malfunctions of the metabolic cycle, because it links brain and body, perceptions and senses to the fragile constructs of our personality.

Digestion, for example, is often a crucial key in this process. Poor nutrition creates poor digestion and poor digestion creates poor nutrition. This has many effects in a person's life on every level, psychological, emotional, intellectual and physical. It can cause many physical health problems and also damage a person's life force so that they are unable to fulfil themselves.

Tibetan medicine aims to correct any long-term problems in the metabolic cycle of a patient's health so that harmony of mind and body become regenerated through the self-correction functions of the metabolism and the seven bodily constituents. By improving the digestive and nutritional cycle, the body is capable of returning itself to health.

> *David had suffered from poor digestion for years and had also developed a minor but painful bowel problem. He decided to follow Tibetan dietary wisdom, and instead of eating raw food, he heated it gently. He also ate less food in general. Not only was he not irritating his digestive system but he was able to absorb more nutrients from his food. His digestive problems improved, his skin, hair and nails became much more healthy and he generally had much more vitality.*

Each of the seven constituents creates a spiritual, physical and psychological dimension, and it is these seven multi-dimensions of the constituents that act as a link with our body and mind. The psychological dimension of every constituent is supported by the humours. In this way the constituents influence our senses, emotions, reflexes and auto-immune system. As the foundations of your metabolism, their effects are so profound that, as they are processed in all your mental and physical systems, they also process and influence your life.

The constituents link the three humours with your body type and, through this interface, can help guide you to the types of food which will best suit your physical health, optimum weight and mental well being. In the spiritual dimension of each body type, the humours are elevated to support spiritual change. You may find your characteristics in more than one body type, as with the humours, but one will be dominant.

Eating well boosts the seven bodily constituents and supports all of their activities, but a poor diet can destroy the constituents and result in emotional and physical ill health.

Find your body type and your psychological and spiritual dimensions

DANGS-MA

Crucial nutrients from ingested food. (This refers to both the function and the process of absorbing nutrients.)

Body type: Tall, thin, angular bones, slightly gangly, long limbs, slow moving, never gains weight regardless of type of food or amount consumed. This body type is influenced by joint conditions. Pale skin with a far away wistful look. Camouflages body with loose fitting clothes.

Spiritual dimension: The spiritual aspect of this most essential physical function is purity and integrity. This refers to the inner knowledge that enables you to act in a virtuous and beneficial manner both towards yourself and others. It is here that your humours become balanced and these powerful forces start to support you to live a balanced life.

Psychological dimension: The capacity to behave in a non violent manner in thought, speech and action to all people, communicating honestly, clearly and non manipulatively.

KHRAG
Blood made from the essential forces of Dangs-Ma

Body type: Medium height to tall, with a well-proportioned body with wide shoulders, tapering waist, wide hips and firm muscles; healthy glow skin, big eyes and thick lips. This body type is physically full of energy and always on the move, with a physical movement that is very fluid and expansive. Although the body is powerful, it is never threatening. Men and women look similar. This body type is influenced by rapid changes in body temperature.

Spiritual dimension: The ability to see into the core of someone's suffering and to identify with compassion, wisdom and spiritual power so that the person can transform themselves, without your perceptive insight becoming emotionally attached.

Psychological dimension: The power to overcome ignorance in all its forms and to transform prejudice in all its guises, while still loving your fellow human beings.

SHA
Muscle tissues built by the primary qualities of blood.

Body type: Small stature, delicate features, quick darting eyes and pointed ears, thin lips with strong cheekbones, long fingers and toes. Well-defined torso and full of stamina. Because this body type is very food sensitive, eating unsuitable food affects the bodily constituent and causes mood swings or very intense emotions.

Spiritual dimension: The capacity to be humble and serve those less able than you without regret. To be unselfish through loving and to live for others as well as yourself. To avoid being addicted to the charisma that other people attach to you.

Psychological dimension: The determination to go on through hardship as you build yourself or others a new life or consciousness. The ability to love and be loved but not to be owned through loving. It's important not to be overcome by the force of obstructions, but know that they pass by like rain clouds on a summer afternoon.

TSHIL

A particular type of fat tissue used in the creation of muscles.

Body type: Tall, slightly overweight, muscular, dominant body, able to influence others through physical presence. Big hands, prominent knuckles and joints; big thrusting chin, big teeth – everything seems large about this body type. Red in face or slightly flushed. Controlled by sexual desires, this body type may also fight with the forces of addiction.

Spiritual dimension: The potential to understand that you cannot own spiritual insight, enlightenment, wisdom, power or love. You cannot own ownership. All these things you can only pass on.

Psychological dimension: Living well, living your dream, is the act of total responsibility. This dimension drives this body to try and live their dreams.

RUS

The nature of bone manufacture from particular body fats.

Body type: Of medium height or small, full of physically generated charisma and immense power, this body type is rounded, curvy and smooth, sometimes prone to excess body fluids or fats. Adaptable to its immediate environment and able to eat whatever is available without getting ill. This body type is a gauge of the individual's mood, changing as quickly as a barometer.

Spiritual dimension: The desire runs through you to build a spiritual structure that brings people together and yet helps them to know their individuality. Sacred structures of all kinds are the bones upon which spirituality rests, though only for a short time. A bone grows if well fed, so study the nature of bone growth to know yourself.

Psychological dimension: Remember that because people do not know who they are, they cannot know who you are. Every person is worthy of attention and is due respect.

RKANG
The types of marrow made from the formative structures of bones.

Body type: This body type is compact, rigid, and seemingly immovable; mentally has a tendency to be self-obsessed. Dense muscle and body, of any height. The body seems stiff, but is actually and naturally highly flexible; its dynamic energy is physically but quietly expressed.

Spiritual dimension: In the marrow lies the truth, the history, the moment and the future of how things were, are and shall be. How do you extract the marrow of your soul to know how it is made? Give up ego, pretence and knowledge or just study the way your body is? Both perhaps. Knowing how things are means you can change them.

Psychological dimension: Everything is in the marrow; do you really want to extract it? You don't need to force the way to truth. It is inside you, right now.

KHU-BA
Rejuvenating fluids, both reproductive and systemic, created by pith of bodily marrow.

Body type: This body type looks like a mixture of the others, with a slightly flushed skin indicating a strong vitality. This vitality drives both an intense mind and a fast-acting body type with speedy reflexes. This body type cannot stand still: everything moves quickly.

Spiritual dimension: As your body renews, so does consciousness. As your body dies, so does illusion about consciousness. All things within you are rejuvenated; all things come from that which is the first to die.

Psychological dimension: Change is war as far as your mind is concerned. Your everyday mind yells with terror when rejuvenation comes near, for fear that it will not know itself anymore. The imagination of the past holds it back; death without change is preferable to everlasting conscious life. This is what your habitual mind believes. But it can transform itself and know that in this dimension rejuvenation gives birth to consciousness.

Now let us look further into the way in which Tibetan medicine views diet.

THE SIX TASTES

As we now know from the concept of the seven bodily constituents, when food enters our metabolism, it goes through a cycle of seven stages, to produce the life and vitality that is essential for this material incarnation.

The crux of the Tibetan theory of food and diet is the concept of six tastes, which condition and influence the seven constituents and in turn the three humours (see below) and the five elements (see Chapters 6 and 7).

As I have said earlier, all foods have histories and energies that will affect many people, particularly processed and other mass-produced foods. They pass on these effects through the six tastes: sweet, sour, salty, bitter, sharp and astringent. According to Tibetan medicine, these tastes are found in eight groups of foods: grains, beverages, meats, oils and fats, cooked and preserved food, vegetables, fruits and spices.

The six tastes are closely connected with the digestive cycle. For instance, too much sweetness sedates the digestive cycle, whereas too much sour shocks and diminishes its effectiveness. If you eat too much of a salty taste, your digested food becomes stuck in your gut and poisons you. An excess of bitter, sharp or astringent tastes makes food ferment in your digestive tract, which decreases your vitality and emotional balance.

How to use the knowledge of the six tastes

The six tastes play an important part in how each of the three humours (Wind, Bile and Phlegm) influence your body from conception, through life and death. As we go through life the three humours, and your own dominant humour, influence how your body changes. Your dominant humour and most dominant taste/s will indicate what foods are best for you. Tibetan medicine teaches us that there is no one healthy diet for everyone but there are correct foods for creating healthy individuals according to their dominant tastes and humours.

The six tastes regulate and shape how your body feels, functions and looks by influencing the body's metabolic function and overall health. Alongside each taste below is an explanation of how Tibetan medicine regards their influence on our bodies, personalities and lives. As you read this next section, explore which taste or tastes is dominant in your life through the food you choose to eat. Then you can discover which foods and tastes are good for you when you are ill or under pressure. You will be able to see the way in which the tastes influence your dominant humour and thus your general state of health.

You will notice that several foods – chocolate, citrus fruit, oysters and spiced meats, for example – occur in more than one group. This is because they contain multiple ingredients which affect people in different ways.

Chocolate was not, of course, known to the Tibetans, but it can be classified according to Tibetan dietary law. Curiously, chocolate and coffee are the only substances that contain all tastes, elements and humours, and so adapt themselves to everyone. Because they are so adaptable, they can alter the mind and body. If taken regularly, they eventually become a poison to which we can become addicted. Rather than cut them out completely, Tibetan medicine suggests using chocolate and coffee in small doses as a medicine, to sedate and calm.

The six tastes and their properties

SWEET

Foods: honey, brown sugar, molasses, chocolate, milk, ice cream, most raw meats, baked foods, bread, rice, barley, lentils, fish, all grains and pulses, fruits (except for apricots), tomatoes, avocado, root vegetables including potatoes and carrots, celery and processed foods.

What sweet taste does

This taste influences and controls the rate at which your body converts food to energy. Depending on the humoural influence, your body type will influence whether this is fast, slow or a combination of the two. This taste makes the body either crave salt things or like sweet. Low proteins, low fats, high carbohydrates such as milk, fish, rice, celery or anything listed under the sweet taste section are best when the body craves a sweet taste.

Healthy use

In moderation, sweet-tasting foods are nutritious and happy within the body, improving the seven constituents of the body and encouraging them to grow. Sweet foods increase body weight, so are important for the old and young and feeble. Medium sweet foods, such as milk, rice and celery, ease sore throats, suppress coughs and activate wound healing. The medium sweet quality is an anti-toxin, it balances and improves the five senses, and balances the Wind and Phlegm humours.

Excess use: beware!

If there is an excess of the sweet taste in the diet, it will promote the growth of unhealthy fat and body fluids, diminish body heat and vitality, energise the Bile humour and contribute to a wide number of lymphatic, glandular and metabolic disorders, which in turn affect organ function.

SOUR

Foods: milk products, chocolate, ice-cream, cheeses, lemon and other citrus fruits, hot spices, alcohol, pickled food, vinegars, fish, apricots (based upon their effects upon digestion), pineapple, passion fruit, mango and berries.

What sour taste does
This taste regulates the metabolism, influencing the autonomic nervous system, which regulates cardiac muscle and glands.

Healthy use
In moderation, sour foods can help to develop and maintain body heat and appetite, and regulate thirst. This taste also influences the way the body and brain talk to each other, and directs their metabolic functions. Sour foods can regulate diarrhoea and an unhealthy gut, and influence digestion. Sour augments the touch sense and can also activate sluggish Wind humour, improving its movement.

Excess use: beware!
In excess, sour foods awaken the Bile humour, and also influence the Phlegm humour, encouraging physical and mental lethargy. Sour can over-stimulate thirst, causing fever and delirium. Nausea and aching limbs are also linked to too much sour taste in the body. Overuse can seriously weaken immune, lymphatic and metabolic functions of the body, and open up the body to infections and serious organ and system dysfunction.

SALTY
Foods: salt, chocolate, burnt or barbecued foods, fish, cheese, edible seaweed and similar freshwater plants, breakfast cereals, bacon and bacon products, snack foods.

What salty taste does

This taste influences the anabolic and catabolic functions of the body which, according to Tibetan medicine, control how your body makes energy. If you are Wind humour dominant, you will have poor sleep if this taste is out of balance; if you are Bile dominant, you will be agitated and if you are Phlegm dominant you will suffer from constipation or diarrhoea. Eat dark green plants to help this balance.

Healthy use

Many physical obstructions, such as constipation, water retention and sore joints are removed by this taste; it increases the healthy sweat function of the body, activates appetite and maintains body heat.

Excess use: beware!

Too much salty food can encourage a wide range of skin problems connected with the lymphatic system and kidneys, including flaking, peeling or thinning skin, also hair loss. In excess, it encourages premature ageing, decreases body weight through fluid loss, and increases thirst through poor assimilation of fluids. Excess salty taste energises the Phlegm humour.

BITTER

Foods: concentrated and preserved foods, chocolate, alcohol, coffee, Indian black tea (not Chinese or Sri Lankan), lettuce, watercress, asparagus, broccoli, rocket, etc., olives.

What bitter taste does

This taste, more than any other, will influence the effectiveness of your endocrine (hormonal) system, which in turn influences your body shape and also your dominant humour. This taste directs the body type to be sculptured by the humoural influence.

Healthy use

In moderation, this taste will improve the appetite, stimulate memory, stop thirst, limit infections, act as an anti-bacterial and anti-toxic agent, and stop fainting spells. It will curb excess fat, grease, bodily fluids, urine and all forms of excrement, and also stop the Bile humour from becoming imbalanced.

Excess use: beware!

Too much Bitter taste will weaken the body, according to the seven bodily constituents of Tibetan medicine.

SHARP

Foods: pickled foods, processed wild meats, alcohol, dry foods, chocolate, snack foods, chillies, garlic, onions, chives, radishes, ginger, leek, cinnamon, nutmeg, all peppers, culinary dried herbs.

What sharp taste does

This taste will either strengthen or weaken the function of the body's immune system and inflammatory responses.

Healthy use

This taste improves heat to the stomach and gastro-intestinal tract and so aids in digestion, increases appetite and cleans out blocked tubes in the body; the sharp quality helps in healing most throat problems and clears decaying tissue.

Excess use: beware!

In excess, this taste reduces the manufacture of reproductive fluids in men and women, debilitates the body, and increases shivering and fainting. It can decrease mobility in the waist and upper torso. Too much sharp-tasting food can also reduce the vitality in blood and other body fluids and tissue.

ASTRINGENT

Foods: red meat, organ meat, sausages, burnt food, smoked bacon, smoked meats, pâté, caviar and seafood, water biscuits, potato chips, chocolate, alcohol, milk products, toast, peanut butter, nuts, seaweed, courgettes, chicory, Brussels sprouts, spring onions, cabbage, pineapple, grapefruit, turmeric, saffron, gourds.

What astringent taste does

This taste influences the circulatory functions of all the body's systems and its osmotic pressure, quality of blood and the amount of useful fluids in the body.

Healthy use

In moderation, this taste helps wound-healing in joints and organs, depression and low energy. It heals bad complexions and adult acne, gives shine and radiance to the complexion, and helps the skin stay young.

Excess use: beware!

In excess, astringent-tasting foods increase any sensation of bloating of the intestines and stomach and contribute to the puffiness of the abdomen. They restrict physical bodily channels and tubes, encourage weak guts and constipation and quickly debilitate the body. The astringent quality can stimulate overproduction of mucus and lymph, causing flatulence and excess gas of the upper digestive tract, angina and unstable heartbeat. In general, too much astringent-tasting food contributes towards coronary disorders and rapid, unsafe and irregular heart function. It may also lead to foggy thinking.

Healing stress by choosing the right taste at the right time

Major life changes carry with them stress, which can lead to different forms of ill-health, such as weight gain and loss, which we look at below. Eating the right food at these times can lessen the hurt and shock, and increase the opportunities for balance and healing. Tibetan medicine believes that if you crave a certain taste during a time of stress, it is acting as a symbolic guide to something you should do or be to enhance, or help solve, the situation.

For example, if you crave something sweet-tasting in a crisis, it may be that a 'sweet' action would soften the intensity and soothe the crisis. You can apply the same way of thinking to the other tastes. So, just as sweet would create peace and conciliation, so sour would wake up protagonists and make them see sense. Salty would help them see the facts, bitter would reveal if there was any bitterness fuelling dissent, sharp would shock the complacent, and astringent would reveal the truth in people's hearts.

Balancing imbalances

If you yourself feel unbalanced, examine how you feel in the context of the six tastes. Do you feel sweet, sour, salty, bitter, sharp or even astringent? Choose what seems the most apt in describing your state of mind, then eat the opposite.

- If you desire the sweet taste eat astringent
- If you desire the sour taste eat sharp
- If you desire the salty taste eat bitter
- If you desire the bitter taste eat sweet
- If you desire the sharp taste eat salty
- If you desire the astringent eat sharp

The reverse of the above list is also true. This will help to bring balance.

Using the tastes symbolically in this way can act as a powerful channel to your inner knowledge, bringing understanding and insight about situations.

Stress-related weight loss and gain

Stress is as old as humankind and exists in some way in every culture. The ancient Tibetans developed a huge range of stress-busting techniques. One of the most effective is to help heal yourself with food. Tibetan medicine says that the more anxious we are, the more our humours are out of balance. Then one or more of the six tastes will grow in dominance and damage the seven bodily constituents, causing weight problems.

According to Tibetan medicine, two things tend to happen when you get stressed: you either lose or put on a lot of weight. This happens if you eat the wrong foods, which can devitalise the brain and nervous system so that they work poorly. If, for instance, the sweet taste becomes dominant, the body stores more nutrients and these turn into fat. If the sweet taste actually becomes in control of the other tastes, excess fat is deposited deep in our abdomen.

If someone puts on a lot of excess weight very quickly because of stress, their major glandular systems are sick. According to Tibetan medicine, they need professional help.

Eating the right food when you're stressed, however, can dissolve tension, increase poor energy, balance mood swings and help sleep problems. To counter stress-related weight gain or loss, eat any of the astringent, sharp and sour foods listed above, in any combination, over a ten-day period.

Healing the stresses of life with food for your humoural type

In Chapter Six you will have found your dominant humoural type. To help optimise your health and prevent illness, eat the foods in your category below as the foundation of your daily diet.

Wind foods (yellow, orange, white)

Apricots, pineapples, papayas, mangoes, apples, bananas, citrus fruits, plantain fruit, sweet corn, maize, quinoa, honey, chicken, quails, duck, goose, egg yolks, fish eggs (but not caviar), butter, buttermilk, ghee.

Bile foods (pink, red and dark red)

Cooked prawns, caviar, pink or red fleshed fish, cooked lamb, red onions, red cabbage, tomatoes, red peppers, cherries, red grapes, watermelon, red plums, pink grapefruit, a small glass of red wine. Any other pink, red or dark red foods, including red berries.

Phlegm foods (blue, purple or dark brown)

Blackberries, boysenberries, blueberries, aubergine, dates, figs, molasses, seeds, nuts, pure chocolate of seventy percent cocoa or over, rye, rye bread(sour dough), liver, hearts, offal, lamb's kidneys and brains. Any other foods this colour.

Immediate food medicines

Tibetan medicine encourages us to eat foods that regulate our cycles of eating. The foods below act as immediate 'medicines' to balance and increase vitality. Eat them regularly as part of your diet at the times recommended.

Dairy products: Best eaten in the early morning for breakfast and at dinner in the evening. Yoghurts, cheese and milk from sheep, cows, goats and oxen.

Meat, poultry, fish, game: Best eaten in the morning for breakfast or early lunch, then in the early evening for supper. For sick people or growing children, red meat or venison or game with a little fat is essential to make the brain function and so create a healthy mind and body; fat on meat fights infections when it is cooked properly. The leanest meat possible is best for healthy adults. According to Tibetan medicine, it is good to eat meat with fruit, cooked or uncooked, but not with a lot of root vegetables.

Oily fish: fish such as salmon, sea trout, tuna, sardines, pilchards, herring.

Fruit: Eat small amounts throughout the day. Fruit brings peace to the body and mind and, in moderation, is good for stimulating the body to break down excess fat. However, it should not be used as a main food supply (i.e., as in fruitarianism) because it can over-stimulate the sweet taste, sedating the digestive tract and making the consumer vacant and directionless.

Vegetables: Eat regularly at breakfast, lunch and dinner. Root vegetables cooked in a low oven for a long time are good for general health. All vegetables are best made into soup, or cooked lightly rather than raw.

Pulses and beans: Eat on their own or mixed with meat; do not mix with other vegetables as this creates imbalances in the six tastes and seven bodily constituents.

Grains: Rice, oats, barley, millet, corn, buckwheat, quinoa and wheat heal the body and mind rapidly, encouraging balance. Eat on their own or with meat or fish; do not mix with pulses or beans. Do not mix with dairy products, as in breakfast cereal and milk. Long-term mixing of milk and grains creates a dominant sweet taste in the body, leading to stress, low energy and poor concentration, due to poor bodily function. According to Tibetan medicine, the practice of mixing additives with wheat in breakfast cereals, pastries, snack bars and other prepared foods which creates a sweet taste, as above, is the cause of the wheat allergies that affect so many people nowadays. Grains relax the nervous system, increase energy, direct the seven bodily nutrients to the brain, and encourage balanced behaviour and refreshing sleep.

Food is a vehicle to self-knowledge and healing. Understanding how the seven bodily constituents, the six tastes and the three humours connect will enable you to become more empowered about the choices you make in food, diet and health.

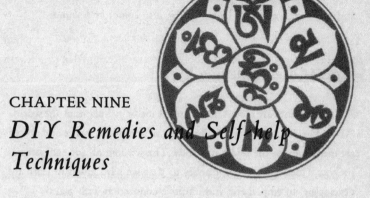

CHAPTER NINE

DIY Remedies and Self-help Techniques

Many Tibetan healing techniques evolved to help people solve minor problems when they were many days journey away from a physician. So there is a rich store of traditional remedies for treating your self and your family. Here are some simple ways in which you can use herbs and spices, massage and hydrotherapy, also colour and sound.

HERBAL MEDICINES

All living things are sacred and so are the medicinal plants of the world. As well as adding flavour to our range of foodstuffs, herbs and spices are medicines for the mind and body. The wisdom of ancient systems, such as Tibetan medicine, teaches us that we have much to learn by developing an empathetic and intuitive connection with plants.

Like animals and birds, all plants teach us about our place in the world. Medicinal plants can allow us to access information about ourselves, as well as balancing our bodies. Using such herbs can help us to reflect upon our lives, our health and our states of happiness and unhappiness.

The survival of mankind over the millennia depended on using plants as medicine. The pharmaceutical drug industry was originally based on phytochemistry and a significant proportion of mainstream drugs today are still made directly from plant sources. Rather than buying them over the counter, you can follow the lead of our ancestors — as many people in the world still do — and use herbs and other medicinal plants to treat simple ills.

Tibetan herbal medicine is a vast and complex store of knowledge, but there are safe remedies you can make at home, using easily found herbs and spices. The purpose of these decoctions and pills is not to bury the condition but rather to encourage the body and mind to heal. Some patients may feel worse before getting better, but this is nothing to worry about. This response is due to the medicine working to create the right balance in the body, and harmonise body and mind.

Please remember that these remedies are for minor health problems that are normally short lived. If they do not improve or seem to worsen, consult your doctor or health professional immediately.

Store cupboard

There are a number of dried herbs and spices that you should keep in your store cupboard to use for a range of common problems: basil (dried but not powdered), cardamom pods (black and green), cloves (whole), chilli powder, cinnamon powder. coriander (dried leaf or powder), cumin powder, garlic powder, ginger powder, juniper berries, liquorice sticks, mustard powder, peppercorns (or ground pepper), saffron strands, sage powder, turmeric powder, and raw organic honey.

These can be made into a decoction to fight and improve the conditions below.

HOW TO MAKE A DECOCTION

Bring one pint (570ml) of fresh filtered water to a boil on a low heat. Cover as it starts to boil and turn off the heat. Cool until completely cold to remove any possible germs and negative energy. Heat the water to a boil again, adding the herbs as below. Cool, strain and use as needed. Store in a clean container in a dark cupboard, or in the fridge. The decoction will stay fresh and safe to use for a maximum of three days, depending on the weather.

Ailments and their treatment

COMMON COLD

To the boiling water, add one level teaspoon of turmeric, five strands of saffron, one stick of liquorice, one teaspoon of sage, one teaspoon of cumin and three cloves. Cover and simmer for fifteen minutes, then turn off the heat, leave to stand until cold, and strain.

Dosage:
- Children over ten years old and adults, two teaspoons of the decoction every two hours until symptoms improve.
- Children from five years to ten years, one teaspoon of the decoction in one tablespoon of cool water three times daily after meals, plus a last cup before bed.
- Very old or frail people and babies from one year old to five years, one teaspoon of the decoction in one tablespoon of warm milk, three times a day after meals.

Warning: Do not give to infants under one year old; it is too strong and will make them ill.

MINOR CHEST INFECTIONS

Put five cardamom pods into boiling water as above, sprinkle a quarter of a teaspoon of chilli powder into the water, and add three juniper berries, half a teaspoon of garlic powder, five strands of saffron, three sticks of liquorice and one teaspoon of cinnamon. Simmer for twenty minutes, cool, then strain.

Dosage:
- Adults: three teaspoons of the decoction, taken every hour.
- Children from five to ten years: one teaspoon of the decoction, in one teaspoon of cool water, before each meal or snack.
- Children from ten to eighteen: two teaspoons of the decoction in two tablespoons of warm water, every two hours.
- Elderly adults: one teaspoon of the decoction in one tablespoon of warm water, every four hours.

Warning: This remedy is not suitable for children aged under five or babies.

POOR SLEEP

To one pint (570ml) of boiling water, as above, add three sticks of liquorice, seven saffron strands, one tablespoon of dark brown organic honey, and half a teaspoon of cinnamon, then simmer for fifteen minutes. Leave to cool until lukewarm and strain.

Dosage:
- Drink one tea cup on the hour for three hours before you usually go to bed.

SORES

To one pint (570ml) of boiling water, add three teaspoons each of basil, sage, ginger, turmeric, garlic and pepper (white or black). Simmer for twenty minutes, then strain.

How to use:
- With a clean cloth, apply the fluid to the affected areas five times daily. Alternatively, soak a cloth in the mixture and place it on the sore for one hour; apply a fresh damp cloth four times a day.

Dosage:
- For adults and children older than ten, drink four teaspoons of the decoction in two tablespoons warm water, four times daily with meals.

Warning: Do not drink on an empty stomach.

CUTS AND ABRASIONS

To one pint (570ml) of simmering water, add four teaspoons of turmeric, two teaspoons of mustard and two teaspoons of ginger. Simmer for twenty minutes on low heat. Cool and strain. This mild disinfectant is excellent in killing infections in minor cuts and abrasions. Apply with clean cloth as needed.

Warning: Do not drink.

CONSTANT FATIGUE

If you lack vitality and feel tired all the time, the following decoction may help. Into a pint (570ml) of simmering water, put four sticks of liquorice, three teaspoons of coriander, four cardamom pods, ten saffron strands and a pinch of grated nutmeg. Simmer for twenty-five minutes, cool and strain.

Dosage:

• One tablespoon every four hours for three days; then drink four cups a day for ten days.

Store cupboard

All of the following ingredients should be powdered or ground: basil, cardamom (black and green), chilli, cinnamon, cloves, coriander, cumin, garlic, ginger, juniper berries, liquorice sticks, mustard powder, pepper (black and white), saffron, sage, turmeric plus raw organic honey, black molasses, corn or barley or rice flour.

These can be made into tablets in order to treat a range of common health problems.

HOW TO MAKE SIMPLE TABLETS

You can mix herbs with rice or barley flour, honey and black molasses to make simple pills. The base is two tablespoons of black molasses and honey (about one tablespoon each) mixed with one tablespoon of barley or rice flour.

Add one teaspoon (5 ml) of each herb in the recipes below, except saffron. Up to twenty strands of saffron should be added, either cut or broken into small pieces, but not chopped.

Roll the mixture into small pea-sized balls and dust with a little more of the flour. Store on a flat tray until dry. You can either leave them in the sunlight or speed the process by putting them in the oven on the lowest possible heat for up to ten minutes, then leave them to dry in the air. Once hard, each tablet will last up to two years.

The tablets can be swallowed with a little water.

Ailments and their treatment

SORE THROATS

Blend together one teaspoon each of cloves, black pepper, turmeric and coriander, and then mix into the base.

Dosage:
- Take one pill four times a day. Take them just before eating and before bed, with a little water.
- Pregnant women should halve this dose.

POOR DIGESTION AND FLATULENCE

Mix together one teaspoon each of sage, cumin and cinnamon, with five saffron strands, and one teaspoon of coriander. Blend with the base.

Dosage:
- Take one pill every three hours.

Herbal fire

Both Buddhist and Bön medicine uses herbs spiritually and ritualistically. When my teacher used herbs for rituals he would have a fire burning for a long time. When it had burnt down, he would sprinkle on the herbs and incant mantras to invoke the deities and spirits of the elements, or to heal people or situations from a distance.

You can simply sprinkle a little of any of the herbs on charcoal, on a live fire, or carefully on a candle flame. Here are some simple suggestions.

Turmeric: For a low mood, negative environment, blocked sinuses. If you are feeling depressed and don't know why, or you feel that your environment is full of negative thoughts, sprinkle a little turmeric on a flame, as above. The acrid smell clears confusion. Inhaling the aroma clears the sinuses.

Ginger: For shock, conflict and sore throats. Burn some powdered ginger as above to clear shock and emotional pain. The bittersweet fragrance will also help to unite people who are separated by arguments, and heal broken trust. Ginger drives out divisive energy. Inhaling its smoke is good for sore throats.

Saffron: To purify the environment and for weak eyes and lungs. Burn ten strands of saffron on charcoal, in a fireplace or simply ignite the little pile of saffron with a match, to create an influx of higher spiritual energy and purify the environment. The dark pervasive smell of burning saffron brings love and breaks down obstructions and fear. Inhaling its smoke is good for weak eyes and weak lungs.

Garlic: For violent thoughts, unwelcome people and germs. The smoke of burnt garlic drives away violent thoughts and action, and cleanses the environment of germs and the imprint of undesirable people. Inhaling its sweet smell calms nervous people and removes psychological pain.

Cinnamon: Burning this spice brings harmony and creativity, encourages happiness and brings clarity of mind and energy.

Nutmeg: Burning nutmeg stimulates shifts in perception about complex problems. It attracts money to the place where it is burnt, but that also brings the responsibility of wealth so you must be prepared to work for and with that money. Inhaling nutmeg may help improve skin infections.

Black and/or white pepper: Burning either type of pepper encourages learning and concentration. Its acrid pungent smell removes bad odours from the environment. Inhaling the aroma can help to heal mouth ulcers.

Basil and sage: When burnt these herbs relieve stress and change discord into joviality. They encourage memories from the past to resurface, engendering sentimental thoughts. If inhaled they can act as an aphrodisiac, stimulating powerful displays of sexual passion. The aroma can also influence people towards acts of piety and kindness. When burnt, these herbs can enable you to influence other people in the same environment.

Ground or whole juniper berries: Juniper has many sacred uses in Tibetan spiritual beliefs; in Buddhist and Bön teachings this herb is used to invoke deities, purify buildings and create a sacred environment. The sweet dry smell of the berries can induce a state of concentration that aids meditation, prayer or any form of worship.

DIY MASSAGE AND OTHER SELF-HELP TECHNIQUES

In modern times, massage has been relegated to a lesser role in Tibetan medicine, but it is still regarded highly by ordinary Tibetans. It can be used for all ages, from babyhood to old age. Massage has the power to ameliorate all manner of physical conditions, both acute and chronic, as well as stress-related problems and severe psychological and psychiatric conditions. In addition to being part of the Tibetan range of therapies, it is also used to prevent illness and for general well-being.

There are many different types of massage techniques in Tibetan medicine, and an experienced practitioner will carry the therapy out using different forms of external medicines as part of the treatment, but let us focus on what you can do for yourself and for your family and friends. It's simple to do and completely free.

Whole body massage for vitality and well-being

You don't need to use oil but, if you do, it's best to use an unscented massage oil. Using the palm of your hand, massage with anti-clockwise circular movements away from the heart.

Start with your torso, and then go on to your neck, arms, wrists, hands and fingers. Use your right hand to massage the left side of your body and limbs, and vice versa (if you are massaging another person you can use the hand that feels most comfortable). Rub around the edge of each finger and the fingertips with the opposite palm. Next move to your inner and outer thighs, mid to lower back (starting wherever you can reach), then your buttocks, legs, heels, ankles, feet and toes.

Do this as vigorously as you can for ten minutes, twice daily, for ten days, when you wake up and just before you go to sleep. It will improve circulation and body tone, help to balance the three humours, aid digestion, calm stress and, in general, enhance your body's ability to work and rest.

At the end of ten days, have a two-day break so that the body can absorb all of the benefits of the massage, then repeat again.

This massage is safe for everyone, so make it a regular health habit for you, your family or friends. For old people and babies, or anyone else in fragile physical health, massage carefully and gently. When you are massaging another person, keep to a slow rhythmic movement and ask them about the pressure they prefer. Try to feel the shapes and contours of their body.

Tibetan acupressure for minor complaints

The Tibetan form of acupressure is safe, simple and helps to boost well-being, as well as relieving minor problems. This traditional self-healing technique was developed thousands of years ago by the homemakers and farmers of Tibet. They used it as an effective treatment when they or their family or neighbours were ill or in pain and a physician was not on hand. Later, the system was adopted and refined by physicians.

As with all acupressure systems, the points are on channels (or meridians) that relate to physiological and energetic structures of the mind and body. The Tibetan system is based on the flow of the three humours, elemental energies and pulse functions.

HOW TO GIVE YOURSELF ACUPRESSURE
Use your index finger or your thumb, or both together, pressing down firmly on the point as you count to 100 slowly. Release for the count of ten, and then repeat five times.

Conditions treated: nausea, diarrhoea, stomach pain and gas caused by overeating, bad food or mild poisoning
Acupressure point: centre of each palm and on each fingertip.

Conditions treated: travel sickness, headaches caused by the common cold.
Acupressure point: middle of each wrist upper and lower, each ear lobe, front and back.

Condition treated: mild joint pain.
Acupressure point: middle of each inner elbow.

Conditions treated: poor vitality, muscle pain, stress-related conditions.
Acupressure point: either side of the chest above the breastbone.

Conditions treated: blocked sinuses, insomnia and sleeplessness.
Acupressure point: the mid point between your eyebrows.

Conditions treated: overwhelming fatigue, anxiety, headache, upper neck pain.
Acupressure point: in the middle of your forehead, just below your hairline.

Conditions treated: stiff neck, frozen shoulder, stiff shoulders and arms.
Acupressure point: at the base of your neck where it meets your spine.

Conditions treated: muscular pain in the spine and general stiffness.
Acupressure point: either side of the spine in the middle of your back.

Condition treated: back pain.
Acupressure point: in the middle of each buttock.

Condition treated: sore or stiff legs.
Acupressure point: in the middle of the folds behind each knee.

Conditions treated: toothache, backache, and constipation.
Acupressure point: the middle of each instep.

Condition treated: general debilitation.
Acupressure point: the tips of each big toe

Conditions treated: overindulgence, chronic illness, joint injury, repetitive injury (such as repetitive strain injury; RSI), or continual hurt to a back.
Acupressure point: the middle of each sole, four times a day.

Hydrotherapy

Hydrotherapy was and is still used in Tibetan medicine to restore vitality to illnesses caused by the three humours, Wind, Bile and Phlegm. Typically, these might be stress or addictions of any kind which result from Wind imbalance, joint problems, digestive disorders or skin conditions related to Bile problems, or infections leading from a Phlegm disorder. In ancient times, a physician would sometimes instruct a patient to stand under a powerful waterfall, to be sponged in hot or cold water or to sit in a type of Tibetan sauna. Today, you can use Tibetan hydrotherapy techniques if you have access to a sauna and a powerful shower.

Hydrotherapy guidelines:
- Do not use a sauna after you have drunk alcohol (even a small amount) or eaten food. Always drink 1.75 pints (one litre) of pure water before doing these hydrotherapy treatments and 3.5 pints (two litres), if possible, in the two hours following your sauna.
- Always rest for at least fifteen minutes after doing any of these hydrotherapy treatments.

SAFE AND SIMPLE DETOXES USING A SHOWER OR SAUNA

For joint problems, skin conditions and general fatigue:
- Stand under a warm shower for ten minutes. Get out and without drying yourself go straight into the sauna for five minutes. Repeat this cycle five times.
- After finishing, thoroughly towel yourself dry; do not worry if you sweat a little.

For stress and the common cold; to prevent flu and bronchitis, and to ease the effects of rheumatism and arthritis in the early stages; to help recovery from long term illness:

- Take a hot shower, as hot you can stand it, for exactly two minutes. Go straight into the sauna for two minutes. Then take a very cold shower, as cold as you can, for two minutes, then go into a sauna for exactly five minutes.
- Take a warm shower for five minutes, then back into the sauna for a minimum of three minutes, up to ten minutes if you can.
- Then dry yourself thoroughly.

For hangovers but *not* if you are still very drunk in the morning:

- If you feel rough or you have a mild hangover, drink two glasses of warm water mixed with lemon juice or strong ginger tea.
- Shower in very warm water for ten minutes.
- Go straight into the sauna for five minutes.
- Take a lukewarm shower for ten minutes.
- Go back into the sauna for five minutes.
- Take a hot shower for one minute.
- Towel yourself dry thoroughly, and with vigour.
- Drink lots of water, then rub the soles and balls of your feet very hard, ten times on each foot.

For the effects of anxiety, panic, stress and fatigue brought on by shock, work or any other life experience.

- Undress and towel yourself all over your body as hard as you can with a clean rough towel. Don't leave out any part of your body, including the top of your head, behind your ears, ankles, feet and toes, hand and fingers, lips and nose.
- Take some fresh basil or sage leaves and step into a hot shower.

- Stroke the herbs all over your body as you shower for one minute. The water must be as hot as you can handle.
- Go straight into the sauna with your basil or sage leaves, tear them up and rub them all over your body. Take what is left and put them in a little pile near you.
- Sit quietly in the sauna for eight to fifteen minutes inhaling the aroma of the herbs. Shower in warm water for five minutes.
- Then finish and towel yourself dry vigorously.

TIBETAN COLOUR HEALING, MOON POWER AND THE SEASONS

According to Tibetan wisdom, every season has a colour. Although the Tibetan calendar and season organisation is different to ours, the wisdom of the seasons translates very well, so we can use colour to balance our humours and create good fortune in our careers, personal lives and spiritual endeavours.

WINTER: DECEMBER THROUGH TO EARLY FEBRUARY

Winter is the season of insight and the maturing of wisdom. It is the time for reflection and balance. This is the time to consider your actions and plan for the future based upon your past experiences. It is also the time to purify yourself.

The winter full moon is white, so, each month, put white flowers, fabric or objects in your home or workplace. Tune into the full moon by reflecting on it and the white objects, thinking how they may purify your mind and body, and the environment around.

At the end of the full moon cycle, place a white flower or a little piece of white cloth into running water; this takes away your impurities and creates positive energy.

SPRING: MID FEBRUARY TO THE END OF APRIL

Spring is the cycle of happiness and discovery. All things can be healed in this season.

The colour for spring is red. On the day of each new moon in springtime, fill your house or workplace with red objects. Wear red if you wish. Focus on the new moon, on its symbolic red colour, and its capacity to bring you all the vitality of spring, to heal you, to cleanse your mind and body and to lead you to happiness.

To strengthen the effect bury one of the red objects you used in this exercise in your garden or in a pot of earth; it will bring you the power of spring throughout the year.

SUMMER: MAY TO OCTOBER

The nature of summer is one of expansion, realisation and conscious awareness of who you are and what you can be. It is the reminder that all things come to a fruitful apex before they fade away to be born again. Summer is the season of birth and death, of renewal and reconstruction and resurrection – a reminder that all energy reincarnates through differing forms.

Gold is the colour for summer. In the first few weeks of summer, fill your house and place of work with golden objects reflecting the colour of the golden summer moons. On each waxing moon, tune into the unfolding of prosperity and feel at one with yourself, the world and the universe. The moon will bring you contentment, insight about the way you live and protection to your household and loved ones. Just before the end of summer, in the last few days of October, place one of the gold-coloured objects into a fire and it will release the energy of abundance and connection with nature.

AUTUMN: VERY END OF OCTOBER UNTIL THE START OF DECEMBER

Autumn is very dark green in colour. On each waning moon, fill your home and workplace with dark green objects and wear something in that colour.

The waning moons can give you a connection to the power of autumn. Tune into November's waning moon and draw its powerful energy to you so that your problems, obstructions and difficulties are washed away.

On the last waning moon of this season (you can check this in a lunar calendar; many diaries and astrology columns also include this information), take a piece of green fabric or some green-coloured seeds and cast them into the autumnal winds so that they are scattered far and wide. As you do so, infuse these objects with all the energy that you have created throughout this autumn lunar ritual. In this way, you are spreading the power and blessing.

HEALING WITH SOUND AND VIBRATION

Sound is vibrational. Nature is vibration. Billions of vibrations give you shape and form. Tibetan medicine has used this knowledge since ancient times. However, the formal version of sound and vibrational healing is a very profound and ancient skill that only a true master should do and carry out. Rather than trying expert techniques such as overtone chanting, you can simply tune into the sounds of nature that are all around you, all of the time.

Here is a simple and safe method for tuning into sounds and subtle vibrations in order to heal and harmonise ourselves. Sit comfortably in a chair, with your back supported and your feet flat on the floor. Close your eyes. Lift up your hands straight up above you, as far as you can, and let your palms and fingers relax.

Using your mind, direct all of your attention into the palms of your hands and your fingers. You have the ability to feel the vibrations of your environment in your hands and fingers. Think of them as antennae which allow you to 'feel' sounds.

Imagine that your hands and fingers are starting to tune into all of the sounds and vibrations around you – people talking, rush-hour traffic, the sounds of nature, anything. As this happens, your hands and fingers may want to move or just be still, let them do what they want. They will automatically filter out unpleasant sounds and vibrations that might cause you to feel upset or uneasy, leaving only instructive, uplifting and positive experiences.

As you listen with your hands and fingers it is like playing a gigantic harp in your mind.

Use the sounds and vibrations to heal you, ease you and help you to develop vitality. Try to do these exercise twice a day for ten minutes each time.

CHAPTER TEN
Living, Loving and Dying

One evening when my soul was newly made, my teacher and I sat looking out across a lake in a mountain range in the North Island of New Zealand. We gazed at a mountain, at an arc of shooting stars, at the moon shy behind wispy clouds. I asked my teacher, 'What should I learn now?'

'You must know how to die and come back to life again,' he chuckled loudly. 'Death is everywhere, mixed with life. Feel it, understand it.'

I looked at the mountain across the valley. I felt it look back at me. It welcomed me, unfolding like a flower. I sent my soul into it and I learned of its birth in the time when time did not matter, of the land from which it rose, and of the plants and animals upon it, and I felt young, small and at the start of the human species.

Running through these perceptions of the soul, like veins of gravity, was death. When I looked into death I saw that it was not a dark void but a brilliant black diamond. Within it was the gateway to liberation, in this life and all others.

I looked back to the mountain. 'Mountains are libraries,' murmured Ürgyen. I could sense that this mountain held the wisdom of the earth and I had learned that the knowledge of death and the knowledge of the earth were connected.

I questioned my teacher again: 'What should I have? What should I be?' A few minutes passed. He leaned towards me, whispering. 'The power of a Ngagpa, the essence of a child, the wisdom of a philosopher, the healing of a mother and the personality of a mountain.'

THE GIFTS OF DEATH

Many people in the West believe that no one can talk about death with any real insight because no one has really died and come back to fill in the details. Tibetan wisdom, however, states very clearly that all of us have returned from the dead. Birth is only one half of death, according to the Tibetans, with life squeezed in between the two.

At the moment of death we are initiated into the great mystery of ourselves – the light of liberation. If we can hold on to the moment when we have the chance to be in this light and ascend into the height of this experience, then understanding of self, life and death is ours.

We should start to think of death in all its aspects as part of our life experience. This does not mean you need to visit a cemetery regularly or keep the bones of your best friend under your bed, rather, contemplating death enables you to look into the most profound aspects of your consciousness, where life and death live together.

Living and dying are the same experience. Within ourselves and our lives, within our experience of death and possible rebirth, are varying states of consciousness: waking-consciousness, dream-consciousness, meditative-consciousness, death process-consciousness, the consciousness of reality and rebirth consciousness. We experience all of these states every day and every night in everything we do, from brushing our teeth in the morning to the dreams we have at night. As we die, our sensitivities become heightened and these states of consciousness become more transparent, allowing us to see them clearly. In the West we talk about the whole of a dying person's life flashing before them before facing judgement. Tibetan wisdom believes that those who are dying re-experience their lives, intensely and rapidly, both the good and the bad. The goal of this is that we gain self-knowledge and redeem ourselves, entering into a state of balance and peace. The danger is that we may be overwhelmed by these extremes of emotion. That is why the Tibetans place such importance on looking after the dying.

Another important thought to hold on to when looking at death is that the force of the universe is the same force as the human mind. They are constructed in the same way. In the process of dying and attaining spiritual liberation, the dying person is encouraged to hear with their intuition universal truths as well as personal ones. We become able to grasp reality – that profound and intimate moment in which you truly discover your innocence and inner knowledge – in a spontaneous way. I hope that, in a similarly spontaneous way, you will be able to experience a connection with the ancient Tibetan wisdom of death and the art of dying.

Many people are afraid of death, but if we can come to associate ourselves with eternal energy, death loses its fear. At any important times in our lives, including the time of dying and death, we are brought closer to experiences of spiritual potential. This is specifically true as we die. During this in-between state, the dying person has access to opportunities for spiritual rejuvenation. Some of the experiences can be very frightening, because of their intensity, while others are comforting. Beneath them all, though, exists the essential energy and light of reality.

In death as in life, people can become confused, so Tibetan culture evolved ways to help people through this challenging time. It is challenging not only for the dying person but also for those who are left behind. In ancient teachings on death and dying, it is taught that the dying person becomes highly vulnerable to the powerful emotions of those who are grieving their loss and this can result in intense pain. Both in Buddhist and Bön teachings, there are texts and oral teachings designed to guide everyone involved in a dying process to a better state of mind. Normally a spiritual teacher reads the texts; in their absence a sincere friend guides their dying comrade to happiness.

Spiritual teachers within the Tibetan traditions usually know all the guides to dying by heart. Many are in the forms of prayers dedicated to compassionate deities that come to aid people through the scary moments of dying and into the beauty, fulfilment and self-knowledge that intersperse them. The most important thing that Western readers can learn from this view of death and dying is that whatever we have done and whatever we have believed or not believed, we can transform our lives as we go through the different stages of dying.

My teacher would often be asked to guide dying people who were not Tibetan, but who wanted a way of bringing their life to an integrated conclusion. Once he was asked to help someone who lived far away. He invoked the consciousness of the person by making a picture of him on a clean white piece of paper. This ritual image, or 'jangbu', was laid on an altar. Then my teacher talked to the dying person, explaining all the possible experiences to come including the different realms of existence and their qualities.

After that, he took the drawing between his two middle fingers and held the image over the flame of a butter lamp. As the flames consumed the image, he announced that all the unskilful actions and thoughts of this person had been cleared and purified. Tibetan wisdom believes that, in the flames, the reformed consciousness of the subject finds its journey to a more fruitful life than the one it has just left.

Just as my teacher had finished this ritual, his telephone rang. It was the family of the dying person. As he had died, a radiant light had emanated from him, they told my teacher. The room had filled with many coloured lights and sweet smells and the assembled family members and friends had experienced profound joy and calm.

A NEAR-DEATH EXPERIENCE

Some people who have died return to the world and tell others of their experiences. My teacher told me this story about Latri Gyalwa, a real Tibetan person, who had been studying how to build a soul when he had this experience. This is the story I was told.

Latri Gyalwa lost all his vitality to an incurable illness that came out of the blue. He began to die and as he started to cross from this world into the in-between state, he began to apply the little he could remember about creating a soul. For many days, he felt blown about like a flower on a strong wind. Then suddenly a guide appeared: a resplendent and radiant female being, whose appearance changed constantly from Jamma the Loving Mother to a mysterious woman whose face he could not see.

On their journey, he met many people who taught him about the nature of birth and death. He learned to respect all living creatures, to be a good person, and to value spiritual insight and spiritual teachers in whatever form or circumstances they might appear. After what seemed an endless time, he briefly encountered various lords of the dead. But much to the shock and amazement of everyone gathered around his deathbed, he returned to his body to tell them about what he has learned.

Not every person who had these near-death experiences in Tibet had them validated as real by their teachers. If they did — as with Latri — the people were known as a 'de-lok'. The near-death experiences of the de-loks, which have been remembered or written down, are very similar to those of people who have had near-death experiences in the West.

Now let us go further into two important aspects of death: how to prepare for death – which also helps you prepare for living – and how to help the dying to die well, a crucial skill which can help to heal everyone and overcomes all prejudices. These two aspects of the death process are embodied in the following five points of understanding. Consider them well. It is essential to accept and reflect on these points in order to benefit from Tibetan wisdom about death and dying.

The five points of understanding death and dying:

- Understand in your own terms what death is.
- Understand that it is important to be aware of this.
- Understand techniques for preparing ourselves for death.
- Understand the stages of the death experience.
- Understand the help that people need as they die.

Over the following pages we will explore the Tibetan view of death and your own feelings about death. We will contemplate the nine ways of death and learn how to create happiness and die peacefully, with self-knowledge and empowerment.

THE TIBETAN VIEW OF DEATH

Life is transitory so we must learn how to live our time carefully and with discretion. Tibetan spiritual practises of all traditions teach that awareness and meditation on death are vital in developing our consciousness. By understanding the death experience, we lose our fear of it and can start to transform all the other turbulent emotional processes that will come to the surface at the time of our death and dying.

Death and dying are two different experiences. Dying in calmness and mental clarity ensures calmness and clarity for those who mourn you and guides us to a better rebirth. Death is viewed as a permanent split of mind and body by the Tibetans. Our minds continue after our bodies have died and then take a new body as best they can.

All of us have had countless numbers of lives with little or no control over what type of lives they are. As we learn to gain control of this process, we can begin to become more self-determining. All our thoughts and actions, speech and deeds, written words and aspirations from previous lives leave their mark upon our minds, like old layers of French polish on a piece of tatty furniture. These marks can be good, bad or in-between, depending upon our actions (karma means 'to act').

As we clean off each layer, we can gain insight about our karma. Remember, though, that while it is important to consider the legacy of karma from previous lives, it is far more important to concern ourselves with our karma in this life, as I explained in Chapter 3.

 YOUR FEELINGS ABOUT DEATH

Your individual state of mind is very important as you die. It influences how you will cope with the experience of dying and how you will be born into a new form of existence. By contemplating death, you can start to treat your life with more sacredness, which will bring you peace of mind and a greater connection to reality.

In order to help ensure that we have a good death, we must try to work upon ourselves while we are living. Stop and think seriously about how you view death. You may think you have no thoughts or opinions about it at all but, deep within, you are bound to have feelings about it. All these feelings can help you understand death. The emotions that attach themselves to death, both your own and others, usually include fear, loneliness and anger. A sense of powerlessness is also a common experience. These emotions often seem crushing, but remember that dying people also feel a sense of peace, acceptance, spiritual joy, forgiveness and a total sense of release from hardship and pain.

Anger is the biggest emotion that causes suffering of intense proportions for dying people, and often causes them to be reborn in a less desirable life than they really deserve. Transforming negative states of mind is the hardest work we face – it is easier to conquer another country than to start releasing the negativity within.

Consider also that reality, as we experience it, is created by patterns made primarily of random thoughts that collide with each other, causing massive amounts of energy to be released, which give form and substance to our lives. These random thoughts could be anything from 'I must pick up the laundry' or 'What shall I have for dinner?', to 'What is the meaning of life?' The process of dying and death reveals this random reality.

Many of us are uneasy about the whole idea of death and our culture tries in the main to ignore it. In fact, ever since the first human being realised that death was here to stay, there have been some basic reasons for why we feel so unsure about death. They are:

- Ego: We believe that each of us is an independent, self-existing personality, so how can this personality just stop? Suddenly we know that nothing lasts forever and this includes us. According to the Tibetan view, this is where all our troubles start.
- Lack of trust: Death creates so many uncertainties for us. Few of us know what goes on as we die, what happens after or why we die, and we are reluctant to trust people who say they do know about it.
- Fear: We are often scared that our death will be painful. We feel isolated by the idea of death and worried about those we leave behind.

All these notions seem valid. You probably know people who have gone through them or experienced them yourself. But they do not really take place within our inner consciousness. They are fears which we have absorbed, since childhood, from other people. Peace of mind comes from recognising that, although they feel real to us, these fears are fantasy. Studying the nature of death helps us to know that we can be the authors of our own death as well as of our life.

CONTEMPLATING THE NINE WAYS OF DEATH

There is a direct relationship between our fears of living and our fears of death. Many people are afraid of life and its uncertainties because they feel that life is more powerful than they are. They are like this because they do not know how to change their inner state. The majority of dying people experience the same mental confusion. So it is important to have in place simple structures to remind us of basic truths.

The nine ways of death can do this for us. Reflect on them as often as you can. These nine ways of death are common to both Buddhism and Bön and are known by slightly different names in various spiritual traditions of Tibet. The nine ways are broken into three main areas of discussion.

We all are going to die:
1. Each one of us is dying right now, but in very tiny segments.
2. According to Tibetan wisdom, our life span is getting shorter in this particular stage of the world's time cycle, due to the spiritual pressures of overpopulation
3. We treat death as if it only happens to other people

Death comes without warning for many people:
4. No one knows when they will die.

5. Our physical body is not indestructible and does not live forever, no matter how we look after it

6. Dying is a natural process and there are as many ways of dying as there are people

Spiritual practice helps us at the point of death:

7. Spiritual practice will help us to die well and gain inner happiness; it doesn't matter what it is, or whether or not we understand it.

8. Nothing we own, have worked for or achieved can guide us through the dying experience; our physical body cannot assist us, its time has ended.

9. Our loved ones cannot come with us or make death easier. They can only wave goodbye. Equally, however, your enemies cannot harm you, animosity will be left behind.

Consider how the body stops working just before death

Within Tibetan medicine and spiritual teachings there are many techniques used for understanding the death process and all the signs of death. You can start to familiarise yourself with it by thinking about how the body of a dying person slowly stops working as they grow near to death. Imagine what that looks and feels like; if you have spent time with a person in the process of dying think back to that experience. Relate the process to your life as it is now. Being near the dying can be helpful so you might consider working as a volunteer in a hospice.

How to help other people who are about to die

We can help others firstly by helping ourselves. Let us look at the following steps, which reflect everything we have learned in this book.

- Try to develop an acceptance of death. Do not be afraid of the process. As you understand more about death, so your fear will lose its sting.
- Try to live as best you can and be as good as you can. In particular, avoid killing, stealing, greed, anger, lust, aggression, using inappropriate sexual energy, or inappropriate and unskilful speech and language. These actions can cause death to be unpleasant because they create immediate psychic side-effects and diminish your vital energy.
- Find a way to understand your mind through a spiritual, religious or ethical practice. Try to develop love for yourself and compassion for all living creatures. Find a practice that feels right for you, and then work hard to apply it. Whatever you do will help you if you are sincere. Following a spiritual practice puts death into its true perspective as another part of your cycle of life. My teacher taught me a contemplation practice that gave me insight about my life, my death and my self. This exercise is called 'The Five Benefits of Developing Intention'. It is a powerful self-healing exercise that creates immediate and long-term benefits in all parts of your life. It activates a powerful compassion that can eventually liberate you from your own mental restrictions.
- Focus upon whatever spiritual belief you have and see it purifying you, your speech, actions, thoughts, mind and body. Then see it blessing the world around you.
- Create within your mind powerful and positive mental statements that negativity will not damage your inner life, that compassion is always within you and that you are always trying to be compassionate.
- Look at the effects that negative emotions have upon yourself and other people. Consider how you create them, how you attract them and how they cause you damage.
- Pray never to be separated from the compassion and kindness that

exists within you. Pray that other people may also find and keep this compassion and kindness.

• Reflect on how you suffer and why, think of all your hardships, then move on to consider how you can use the experiences to understand yourself more.

Death is our greatest teacher if we just know how to listen to what is being taught. It is important to start as early as possible. In order to understand death and what it has to offer, you must first look at your life. Do this by dividing your life into three sections:

• From birth until 20
• From 21 to 40
• From 41 upwards

If you are under 20, divide your age into three again, from birth until 10, from 10 until 15, from 15 until 20. If you are in the 20 to 40 age groups, take the first category then divide it again from 20 to 30 and 30 to 35, or 30 to 40.

You are going to write down one statement which is the essence of each age group. This is to do with your feelings, not what you achieved or did, but the underlying emotional reality for you at each stage of your life. You can identify the underlying essence of your life through the following meditation, which will show you both the nature of your past and how your life has progressed.

Sit quietly. Start with your current cycle. At first, don't focus upon a particular thing or aspect, just let yourself float; slowly key elements will start to arise. Be gentle and quiet with yourself. You will start to identify the underlying theme. As you do so, direct your breath at it and as your breath passes through, imagine that you are extracting its essence and purifying it from obstructions.

When you are at the second stage, direct to it as much kindness as you can. It then reveals itself. Repeat this with the third stage. Now you can start to reflect upon the themes and learn from them. Rest in this last stage considering what you have found out and its relevance to your life.

This simple practice will bring great insight. Not only will happiness increase and problems decrease, but fear and other mental impressions will become less intense or non-existent. By doing this meditation regularly, you will create a deep inner peace.

When you come to the time for death, this peace will be with you, you will know why you had to die and there will be no fear. On the day you decide to die physically, your inner mental world will become illuminated with the clear light of love and consciousness. You will wake up to a new horizon and your self-created soul – a fusion of intellect and will, imagination and symbolic understanding – will navigate a small but indestructible boat which will guide you across a great ocean to your ultimate destination.

GIVING LOVE AND KINDNESS TO A DYING PERSON

Now let us look at simple and compassionate ways to help those people who are about to die. Giving love and kindness to a dying person is a miraculous act that anyone can do. But often our own fears, prejudices, attachments and ambitions get in the way.

Think instead of all the good experiences you have had in your life. They have been created by good energy. You can direct that same powerful vitality to help the dying person go on their way with more ease and mental clarity.

Everyone's death is meaningful. Sometimes, though, neither they nor those left behind discover the meaning. By following some of the suggestions below, you may help the dying person discover the meaning of their life, and you may discover the meaning of yours.

Honesty, understanding, the desire for freedom, respect, love and acceptance are key in creating a beneficial relationship between the person who is dying and those who are caring. Honesty is important; in this context it means that you should only ever be yourself, the way you are inside is important. Give as best as you are able. Your heart is wisdom; it knows what to listen for, if you let it. Be straightforward and sensitive with how you express your feelings. Remember that at any time you could be in their place.

Understanding comes from your heart's perception of your inter-changes with the dying person. Often it's not what you say that is important. Don't let your ego or theirs get in the way. Do not be a know-all. Be as empathetic as you can, for that is what the dying person needs.

The desire for freedom is often a struggle between the dead person clinging to their memories of life and also wanting to die and be at peace. Sometime a dying person seeks assurances that they can die, that they are not being irresponsible by dying and leaving everyone else to pick up the pieces. Always assist if you can with unfinished domestic matters. This will help the dying person die with fewer attachments to this life and a calm sense from having put things in order.

Another aspect of freedom is that the dying person is able to look back and stop regretting the big events in their lives that they had formerly regarded as setbacks or bad situations. When people die with regrets it slows them down on the path to happiness, and the regrets linger in the minds of those who are left behind.

Always respect the goodness in people. Respect is crucial to a dying person feeling safe and secure, just as it is for those of us who are living.

No one has a right to judge a dying person. They are their own judge, jury and redeemer. Remind them that they are brave and that their example brings hope to other people.

Dying people feel love intensely when it is directed towards them. Love creates an immediate connection which reassures the dying person that they are protected. The very experience gives them hope. Acceptance is crucial in caring for a dying person. One day they will be happy and the next they will be gloomy. Many pent-up emotions can also explode at this time. Don't be offended by what they say. Ignore their words but not their being.

Practically speaking, the best thing anyone can do for a dying person is to make things as uncomplicated as possible, from the physical environment to the visits of friends and family.

Try not to become attached to the dying person because this will act like a psychic glue to them after they are dead. They will want to be with you, and not move on. Listen carefully to whatever a dying person says, for their words are statements of their being, but do not enter into powerful or intense emotional encounters.

It is very helpful to empower a dying person by encouraging them to use whatever spiritual beliefs they have to focus their consciousness. In the room where they are, place some type of uplifting picture, or a statue or image that represents their belief to them. Have it close to them in case they wish to touch it. If the dying person has no structured beliefs or has defined him or herself as an atheist, help them to discover beauty in themselves and in other people. Helping any dying person to focus upon peace and positive examples of life and beauty enables them to experience those qualities. As they do this any fear, anger or other powerful emotion will lose some of its bite.

If you have known the dying person well for a long time, you may see a completely different dimension to this person's character and personality. But if you do, don't force on them anything such as a religious practice – confession, for instance – or mind-changing drugs, with the misguided belief that it is good for them. It could cause them serious emotional injury. And you as well.

The most important aspect of care for the dying person is that they have mental integrity. Encourage them to dwell on freedom and inspire them to hold thoughts of compassion and happiness in their minds as much as possible. If the dying person dies thinking of the wellbeing of others, then that will happen. Focusing on taking the burden of another's suffering, and returning compassion to others, creates a huge resource of positive energy and love. It will also help the person to die with a heightened state of consciousness.

As much as you are able, try to understand the mental patterns of the dying person's mind. If they are open, discuss with them how they have seen their lives. If someone is unconscious, you can communicate with him or her as if they were awake and listening to you. Direct positive thoughts to them; think of the energy permeating through their unconsciousness into their inner selves and transmitting all your good wishes, warm intentions and compassion.

If someone is in physical pain, it is good to use medications to take this pain away. If they are in mental pain, however, it is not good to sedate them because they will die even more confused than they were before they started to die. You can give them positive help by directing emotional calm and love to them, and by improving the colours and ambience of their immediate surroundings, with flowers, for instance.

Dying people are very sensitive to their immediate environment and to the mental energies of other people. Family and other arguments can cause profound emotional pain for the dying person. So peace should be made between everyone.

Finally, don't neglect the lighter side. Dying people love to be entertained so find out what form of art or entertainment they like the most and let them have as much as they want. It acts as a mental food, filling them up with positive energy.

BLESSING FOR THE DEAD

This mixture of prayer, benediction and creation of vital energy is uplifting and profound for those who are left behind. It is designed to help the dead and heal the bereaved.

<~>

Good Friend, you have died,
soon you are about
to leave your body never to return.
Your actions here are finished,
You can take nothing with you on your way.
All regrets, troubles and pain
now no longer have a claim upon you.
Let your face receive the Clear Light.
You are pure now, no blemish or stain.
Hold on to your highest belief.
It anchors you like a kite in the strong wind.
Become unified with the divine.
Let your spiritual friends guide you to unity.
Good Friend, give blessings to all things.
Compassion is with you on your way.

<~>

As you say this, direct a sphere of brilliant white light to the top of the dying or dead person's head. Think of it flowing down through them, purifying their body and their consciousness, into their physical heart. Then direct the light up to the crown and out into the person's field of consciousness.

Do this as soon as the person is dead and each day for 49 days, as the dead person travels through the complex stages of coming to terms with dying. Another thing you can do for the dead person in this period is to be as gentle and compassionate to others as possible and, on the dead person's behalf, study any spiritual belief they may have had. This helps them and it helps you.

Always try to have funeral rites, undertakers and everything else planned beforehand. It makes life easier for you and the dead person. Let there be peace around them and at their funeral. The dead person will be curious about how others see them so they will want to be there, but loud noises at funerals can shock people who have recently died and cause them to panic because they have not fully come to terms with being dead.

AFTER A DEATH

Whether you are a professional carer, a family member or close friend, you will be fragmented after someone dies, even if you don't feel you are. Life is never the same again. Once you have time to reflect, you will probably feel a mixture of emotions: worn out and anxious, relieved and angry, sad and happy. You may feel that life is a mixture of fantasy and reality. You might want to spend time alone then suddenly need to be with people (always do both).

Everyone grieves in his or her own fashion. Share your feelings with a friend or friends, and/or with a professional therapist. Crying can be helpful, but cry for yourself rather than clinging to the dead person. If there was any unfinished business between you and the dead person, give it up, douse it with love and let it go. You are unable to change the past.

If we hold onto memories of the dead person with too much force, we will create intense pain for ourselves and for other people because pain is contagious and can be spread in the emotional atmosphere.

This gentle prayer helps with pain and loss. It invokes healing and directs changes within yourself. My teacher called this particular prayer a 'Zor' – or bomb – of happiness. In Bön, symbolic bombs were used to create transformative experiences in times of death or if there are obstructions in people's lives that could not be moved in any way. You may think that taking on the world's suffering is the last thing you want to do, but if you can be this selfless, the benefits are immeasurable. Say the entire prayer aloud, quietly, addressing it to all human beings and living creatures.

<~>

All the world knows pain and grief,
All living creatures know this to be true.
All living creatures want to be free from suffering
And for pain never to return.
I do.
In this moment I am suffering.
I dedicate my suffering to all Life.
I take all the suffering of other living creatures
Upon me now, in order
That they may be free from grief and affliction.
May all pain of loss and unkindness be vanquished,
All our cruelty shall no longer prowl
as a blood lusting tiger
within us now.
Let all suffering come to an end.
I cast this prayer into the world

And with my pure incoming breath destroy the
Dross and violence of this time
And blackness comes into my heart,
There my pain and loss die
Transformed from out of darkness into the healing
brilliance
Of the clear light,
And as my breath rushes out in power, compassion
and beauty
All beings are free from suffering!

<~>

When my teacher died

A small clay bowl was placed in my hands. It was tied by a white silk scarf that fluttered in the evening wind. It held some of Ürgyen's ashes. His family gave them to me. It was what he wanted, they said.

I was not sad at my teacher's death, for sadness had no place. My teacher had come to an end in this life, but what he was continued on in others and myself. He died well, his mind in good health and his body tired.

I took his ashes back to Mount Pihanga and built a mound of rocks in which I lit a fire. I offered up prayers and blessings to my teacher, his family and his teachers and the world at large. I placed the small clay bowl into the heart of the fire. It began to melt, encapsulating the ashes. I let the fire burn down and, as the melted bowl cooled, it formed into a black sphere of concentrated spiritual power and blessing.

Taking the sphere to the edge of Lake Rotoponamu that sits against the edge of Mount Pihanga, I threw the sphere far out into the lake. Finding the deepest part, it sunk to merge its energy with the water, fire, earth, wind and sky of the volcanic land, there to radiate blessings and strong energy to all living beings. To this very day, the blessing sphere sits within the lake.

I returned to the little shrine of rocks, the fire still smouldering within it. Prayer flags fluttered gently in the evening wind. A purple sky stretched around me and out into the horizon. My teacher's flat drum hummed as the wind ran across its surface. I stared off into the valley below wondering what I was to do with all that I had learned.

Even though my teacher had encouraged me to find a way to bring these teachings to a Western understanding, I still felt uncertain. Then words that Ürgyen had spoken years before came back to me. 'There is no need to doubt, just be at peace and the answers will come.'

I threw more wood into the fire. 'Look for the answers, then you'll know the questions.'

The smell of rain floated on the breeze. 'Nothing is as it seems.' My teacher's voice was faint, distant. I looked up and saw a cascade of shooting stars.

POSTSCRIPT

*E*very aspect and experience of our life, each memory, fear, success, dream or aspiration, is a gift that holds within it the magic of health, happiness and sacredness.

True health has nothing to do with doctors or healers of any type. It is to do with inner purity, power and patience. This comes by understanding the value in our suffering. It means that we have to work hard as we go through the process of physical, psychological and spiritual change.

This is the hardest thing that any person can do and you can only do it on your own. Of course there are others who can help, but ultimately it's up to you.

As you heal yourself you will begin to find your own insight into the nature of knowledge and into the love that exists in all of humanity. Every person is sacred. Every person is Love encapsulated into a special form and personality. Knowing this, even a little connects each of us to happiness because happiness is a taste of the sacred in all things.

Simply by the act of starting to heal your life, you spark the healing of others and of the world in which we live. You don't need to force this idea on other people. The quiet act of living in accordance with who you are and who you can be allows the natural influence of goodness to grow.

As this goodness finds its own expression in other people there comes with it wisdom and knowledge. Knowledge of the natural world and of the inner workings of human nature, of the power of mind and thought in the material world. Ngagpas were the first beings of the ancient world to have this knowledge. They passed it on, not just to their descendants but into the psyche – the spiritual core – of all humanity.

Humanity at large – which includes all of us – has been sick for a very long time. We have forgotten our intrinsic nature. We have lost sight of the knowledge that along with our instinct for survival are the instincts of spiritual wisdom, healing and happiness. When we forget that we have these qualities of inner wisdom we become unhappy. Unhappiness makes us sick. And so the cycle continues.

All we have to remember is that we, all of us, are the cure.

As you start to understand your mind and the nature and limitations of your thought, you will – sooner or later – come to a place of consciousness which is vast and out of your normal experience. Our normal experiences are dependent upon our everyday mind. The everyday mind believes that it has an everyday consciousness so it becomes shy, doubtful and needy, and feels impotent. Exposed to the raw pain of this, many people do not have lives at all: life is an iceberg and they are underwater. Others build an apparently successful life because they contrive to stay on top of the iceberg by dint of paying no attention to the fact that they will slowly melt into this vast consciousness and disappear.

Yet in this everyday self is an essence of higher consciousness that is uniquely who you are. It pervades all things, from sea to sky, from the first to be born and the last to die and you are in communion with all things. Every day becomes one day, a day of gladness and beauty that reinvents itself as you do through the natural delight of creation.

How is this achieved? By developing the ability of balance. This is not the weighing of one thing against the other, or the unskilful action of running from one action to the next, but knowing that true balance comes out only in the spaces between moments. You must not believe in time, but in the effects of time.

In order to know balance, we must know our history. This is not just the passing of events, personal, social, cultural and global, but also the engraving of our consciousness upon our selves. As a species, our biggest injustice to each other and to ourselves – beyond cruelty, war or disease – is that we forget our interconnectedness with all living creatures. We pull ourselves back into the everyday mind and believe we are separate from others, above, below, different and therefore not responsible.

We are not. We are all the face of whatever God we believe in. Although we are all born and die with inequalities, we must strive to attain a common equality that lies not in external achievements but in the spiritual, the unity and the beauty of our humanity.

We are love, wisdom and compassion. We are our greatest achievement and our greatest degradation. We are mystery and clarity. We are the great laughter that anyone can hear when we listen closely to the workings of the universe in nature and our hearts. We are the universe, the cosmos rising up to recognise ourselves. We are the cosmos in descent, bringing down spiritual wisdom to be used in the world of time and the everyday mind.

From infancy, all of us search for an animating principle or experience in our lives. We do this through stories, beliefs and events which are redolent with significance and value. Things beyond our imagination somehow support it, allowing us to transcend our everyday minds. This is the interface where impossible things can be actual and meaningful, where wonder and faith intermingle. Where all things are acknowledged.

Many people consider faith crazy and ridiculous, and it is exactly this. When we have faith, we can move beyond the set beliefs of our society into the absolute freedom of pure consciousness.

The starting place is to go back to the outlook we had as children. Most of us know that young children believe in everything and it is in this mind set that we can develop discernment and consciousness and discover faith.

The first step to faith is the belief in all things, the second is the experience that Everything believes in each of us. This exists within us now. We know this, yet we are afraid. We have this ready to experience, yet we shy away. Opening the door to it is our gift to ourselves.

That is the Tibetan art of living.

APPENDIX

CONSULTING A PHYSICIAN OF TIBETAN MEDICINE

Some readers may wish to consult a physician of Tibetan medicine and I urge you to make sure that whoever you see is qualified and competent. At the time of writing this, there is no register of physicians of Tibetan medicine, either Buddhist or Bön, but an international association is being established.

The first consultation may last from ten minutes to two hours, depending on how the physician views your condition and what is best suited to your needs. Subsequent appointments may take place at weekly, monthly or three monthly intervals. The cost is likely to be from £10 to £100, or a donation, depending on the needs of the physician.

Here are a few simple guidelines to help you get the most from the initial consultation and subsequent treatments.

Ask direct questions and expect clear answers: Don't be afraid to ask questions and to go on asking them until you receive clear answers that you understand fully.

Diagnosis: The 'absolute treatment' is in fact the diagnosis, according to Tibetan medicine. True and accurate diagnosis gives a physician insight into how your mental, emotional and physical systems interact. This insight should activate your self-healing potential and help you to feel peaceful and clear. The physician will usually also tell you the prognosis if you do not make the recommended changes to your lifestyle in terms of food, diet, behaviour etc.

Diagnostic procedures: There are three main techniques of diagnosis:
- The physician examines the patient for symptoms and indications that can be observed in appearance, character, personality and speech; the physician also studies the urine and other bodily excretions, eye and tongue. Take a sample of urine (150–200 ml/5–7 fl oz) to the first consultation.

- Touching the patient with respect and sensitivity, the physician studies pulse, temperature, body growth patterns, skin, bones, finger and toenails, and closely inspects troubled areas of the body. Pulse diagnosis will reveal the nature and types of illness of the patient and, from this, an experienced physician can determine how the complaint first came into being and the best form of treatment. This will help you to understand not only what is wrong but why, and how you can heal both your illness and your life. If possible, try to be relaxed when you see the physician because this can help in carrying out an accurate pulse diagnosis; if you have any spiritual practice or belief, focus on it before seeing the physician. However a good physician can help regardless of your state.
- The physician takes a medical history including dietary and behavioural habits, symptoms, illness and disease, and the effect of season and climate change.

Medication: most traditional Tibetan medicines can safely be taken with Western pharmacological drugs, but make sure that your Tibetan doctor knows and understands any drugs you may be taking because it may affect what they prescribe.

Lifestyle changes: Physicians should be able to deal with all types of influences on your health that affect you at the time of consultation. Lifestyle changes are key to treatment, but they may recommend changes that you are unable or unwilling to make. If this happens, do not be afraid to discuss these and negotiate. If you can, however, and if you trust the physician, it is preferable to carry out his or her advice.

Further information

If you would like to know more about Christopher Hansard's work, and that of the other practitioners at the Eden Medical Centre, please contact:

Sharon Seager
Communications Manager
Eden Medical Centre
63a King's Road
London SW3 4NT
Telephone: +44(0)20 7881 5800

E-Mail: SAS@edenmedicalcentre.com
Website: www.edenmedicalcentre.com

For more information on Tibetan Bön Medicine in Europe, please contact:

Dr A.M. Ritt and Dr Ch. Ritt
Institute for Tibetan Bön Medicine
Schottenfeldgasse 3/12
A-1070 Vienna, Austria
Tel: + 43 1 5224 3369

This Institute is becoming the central point for Bön medical studies in Europe and is also affiliated with the Shen Ting Ling Tibetan Bön Institute.

INDEX